The definitive guide to the leading employers recruiting graduates during 2023-2024.

HIGH FLIERS PUBLICATIONS LTD
IN ASSOCIATION WITH THE TIMES

Published by High Fliers Publications Limited
The Gridiron Building, 1 Pancras Square, London, N1C 4AG
Telephone: 020 7428 9100 *Web:* www.Top100GraduateEmployers.com

Editor Martin Birchall
Publisher Gill Thomas
Production Manager Darcy Mackay
Portrait Photography www.cityspacecreative.co.uk

Printed and bound in Italy by L.E.G.O. S.p.A.

A CIP catalogue record for this book
is available from the British Library.
ISBN 978-1-9160401-4-4

Contents

	Page
Foreword	4
Researching The Times Top 100 Graduate Employers	10
Understanding the Graduate Job Market	22
25 Years of Change for Universities, Students & Graduates	32
Graduate Lives: From University to Britain's Top Employers	43

Employer Entries

	Page		Page		Page
AECOM	66	Deutsche Bank	114	Microsoft	162
Airbus	68	DLA Piper	116	Morgan Stanley	164
Aldi	70	Dyson	118	Mott Macdonald	166
Amazon	72	Enterprise	120	NatWest Group	168
AON	74	EY	122	Newton	170
Arcadis	76	Freshfields	124	NGDP	172
AstraZeneca	78	Frontline	126	NHS	174
BAE Systems	80	Google	128	P&G	176
Bank of America	82	Grant Thornton	130	Penguin	178
Barclays	84	GSK	132	Pfizer	180
BBC	86	Hogan Lovells	134	Police Now	182
BCG	88	HSBC	136	PwC	184
BDO	90	IBM	138	Rolls-Royce	186
BlackRock	92	J.P. Morgan	140	Royal Navy	188
Bloomberg	94	KPMG	142	Santander	190
British Airways	96	Kubrick	144	Savills	192
BT Group	98	L'Oréal	146	Secret Intelligence Service (MI6)	194
Capgemini	100	Latham & Watkins	148	Sky	196
Channel 4	102	Lidl	150	Slaughter and May	198
Citi	104	Linklaters	152	Teach First	200
Civil Service	106	Lloyds Banking Group	154	Unlocked	202
Clyde & Co	108	Mars	156	Vodafone	204
CMS	110	Mazars	158	White & Case	206
Deloitte	112	MI5 - The Security Service	160		

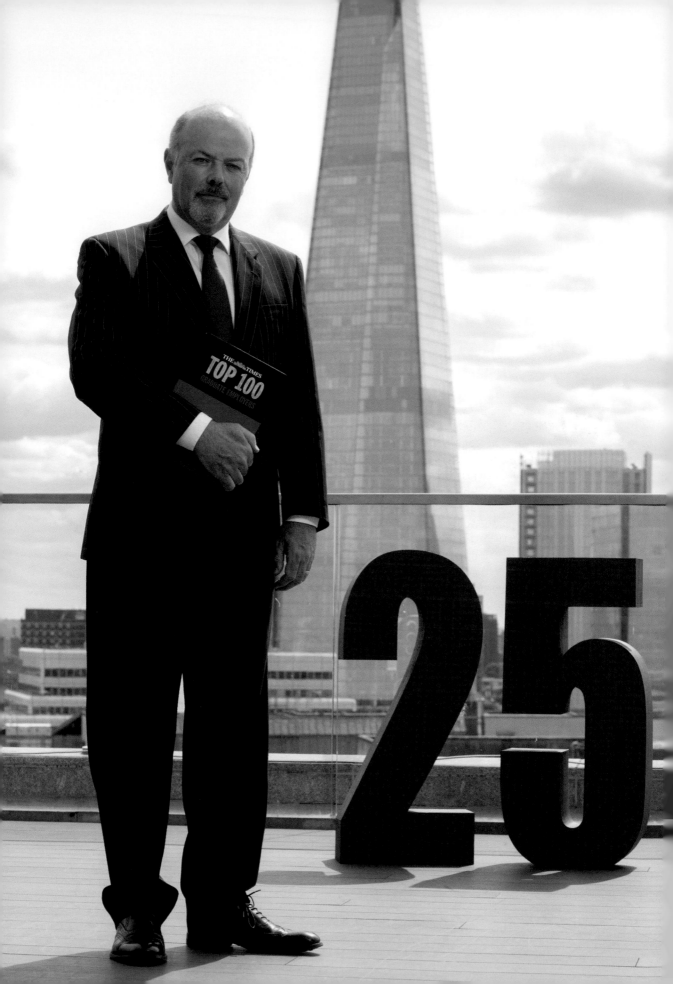

Foreword

By **Martin Birchall**
Editor, *The Times Top 100 Graduate Employers*

Welcome to the twenty-fifth edition of *The Times Top 100 Graduate Employers*, your annual guide to the UK's most prestigious and sought-after graduate employers.

In the autumn of 1999, just as the first edition of a distinctive new red and black careers directory was being delivered to universities around the country, final preparations were being made to open the Millenium Dome (now *The O2*) in south-east London and the London Eye was being lifted into place opposite the Houses of Parliament, in readiness for the Millenium celebrations.

In Europe, eleven countries were getting used to their new 'Euro' currency and in the United States, President Bill Clinton was coming to the end of eight years in the White House.

Back in the UK, Tony Blair's New Labour Government introduced the new National Minimum Wage of £3.20 per hour and the first students to pay £1,000 per year tuition fees had enrolled at university.

Just 20 per cent of the population had access to the internet at home and the best-selling mobile phone of the year was the Nokia 3210. *Star Wars: The Phantom Menace* was the year's most-watched film at UK cinemas and Britney Spears had the best-selling single with *Baby One More Time*.

Graduates leaving university in 1999 emerged into a booming job market. Entry-level vacancies at the country's top employers had increased by an impressive 12 per cent the previous year, one of the largest annual increases in graduate recruitment since the late 1980s.

Starting salaries for new graduates were rising quickly too, by nearly twice the rate of inflation, as the UK's leading employers competed hard to recruit the best university-leavers for their organisations.

Now, as *The Times Top 100 Graduate Employers* celebrates its twenty-fifth year, today's graduates are facing a very different outlook.

Over the past year, the UK has endured its worst cost-of-living crisis since the 1970s – brought on by the aftermath of the Coronavirus pandemic, Russia's invasion of Ukraine, and global energy shortages. Since January 2022, the Bank of England has raised interest rates from 0.25 per cent to over 5 per cent, to try and curb raging inflation, and although the country has not slipped into recession, the UK's economy grew by just 0.2% in the first half of 2023.

For those who left university in the summer of 2023, their early years at university were dominated by the pandemic, with in-person teaching abandoned and extended periods of online learning, and little or no campus social life or extracurricular activities possible. And then the final eighteen months of their degrees have been

" Fewer than half of 2023's graduates thought their time at university had been 'good value for money'. "

blighted by a series of strikes by the University and College Union and most-recently, its nationwide marking and assessment boycott, which left many of the 'Class of 2023' unable to graduate or receive their final degree classification.

According to *The UK Graduate Careers Survey 2023* – the annual survey of final year students that provides the research for *The Times Top 100 Graduate Employers* – fewer than half of 2023's graduates thought their time at university had been 'good value for money' and their average student debt on graduation was a record £43,000.

Despite these very considerable challenges, today's university-leavers are emerging into a highly buoyant graduate job market. Recruitment at the country's leading graduate employers has continued to recover well from the pandemic and employers expect to hire 13 per cent more graduates in 2024 than in 2019, the pre-pandemic peak in graduate recruitment.

Graduate starting salaries are now also increasing rapidly, following more than a decade of little or no growth in graduate pay. Driven in part by the cost-of-living crisis, the average graduate starting salaries on offer at the UK's top employers have jumped by almost 12 per cent in the past two years and are set to increase further in 2024.

The editorial features in this edition of *The Times Top 100 Graduate Employers* celebrate twenty-five years of graduate recruitment at the UK's most successful and sought-after employers. More than 200 individual employers have appeared in the *Top 100* rankings over the past two and a half decades, together providing over half a million graduate jobs for generations of university-leavers.

Since the first edition was published in 1999, more than 1.5 million copies of *The Times Top 100 Graduate Employers* have now been produced, helping students and graduates at universities across the UK to research their career options and find their first graduate job. Over 750,000 job hunters have registered to use *The Times Top 100 Graduate Employers* website – and during the past three years, more than 150,000 students and graduates have read the popular new digital edition of the *Top 100* that was introduced at the start of the pandemic.

A quarter of a century after its launch, *The Times Top 100 Graduate Employers* continues to provide an unrivalled, independent assessment of the UK's most highly-rated graduate employers.

THE TIMES TOP 100 GRADUATE EMPLOYERS
Finding out about the Top 100 Graduate Employers

PRINT & DIGITAL EDITION

Each employer featured in this edition of the *Top 100* has their own **Employer Entry**, providing details of graduate vacancies for 2024, minimum academic requirements, starting salaries, for new graduates, plus this year's application deadlines.

WEBSITE

Register now with the official *Top 100* website for full access to the very latest information about the UK's most sought-after graduate employers.

This includes details of employers' internships & work experience programmes, local university promotions and application deadlines.

And get ready for your applications, online interviews and assessment centres with up-to-the-minute business news about each of the organisations featured in this year's *Top 100*.

www.Top100GraduateEmployers.com

BY EMAIL

Once you've registered with the *Top 100* website, you'll receive **weekly email bulletins** with news of the employers you're interested in, details of their latest graduate vacancies, and their forthcoming application deadlines.

Constant change.
Endless opportunity.
Graduates wanted.

dyson

careers.dyson.com/early-careers

Join our human-led, tech-powered team

pwc

The New Equation is our global strategy to address the breadth and complexity of challenges facing our clients and communities. We work together to build trust and deliver sustained outcomes by combining human ingenuity with the right technology for real results.

Be a part of The New Equation.

To find out more, visit: **pwc.co.uk/careers**

THE TIMES · TOP 100 GRADUATE EMPLOYERS · 2015-2016

THE TIMES · TOP 100 GRADUATE EMPLOYERS · 2016-2017

THE TIMES · TOP 100 GRADUATE EMPLOYERS · 2017-2018

THE TIMES · TOP 100 GRADUATE EMPLOYERS · 2018-2019

THE TIMES · TOP 100 GRADUATE EMPLOYERS · 2019-2020

THE TIMES · TOP 100 GRADUATE EMPLOYERS · 2020-2021

THE TIMES · TOP 100 GRADUATE EMPLOYERS · 2021-2022

THE TIMES · TOP 100 GRADUATE EMPLOYERS · 2022-2023

THE TIMES · TOP 100 GRADUATE EMPLOYERS · 2023-2024

Researching The Times Top 100 Graduate Employers

By **Gill Thomas**
Publisher, High Fliers Publications

In 1999, the year that the first edition of *The Times Top 100 Graduate Employers* was published, there were an estimated five thousand employers, large and small, recruiting graduates from UK universities.

Over the past two and a half decades, the number of employers recruiting graduates has risen steadily and for those due to leave university in 2024 and beyond, there are expected to be more than 200,000 graduate-level vacancies available annually.

But finding the 'right' graduate employer can often be a daunting prospect. What basis can you use to evaluate such a large number of different organisations and the employment opportunities they offer for new graduates after university?

The Times Top 100 Graduate Employers is compiled each year by the independent market research company, High Fliers Research, through interviews with final year students at the country's leading universities.

This latest edition is based on research with 13,309 students who were due to graduate from universities across the UK in the summer of 2023. The research examined students' experiences during their search for a first graduate job and asked them about their attitudes to employers.

Final year undergraduates from the 'Class of 2023' who took part in the study were selected at random to represent the full cross-section of finalists at their universities, not just those who had already secured graduate employment.

The question used to produce the Top 100 rankings was "Which employer do you think offers the best opportunities for graduates?". The question was deliberately open-ended and students were not shown a list of employers to choose from or prompted during the interview.

The wide selection of answers given during the research shows that final year students used very different criteria to decide which employer offered the best opportunities for graduates.

Some evaluated employers based on the quality of the recruitment promotions they'd seen whilst at university – either online or in-person – or their recent experiences during the application and graduate selection process.

Other final year students focused on the 'graduate employment proposition' as their main guide – the quality of training and development an employer offers, the starting salary and remuneration package available, and the practical aspects of a first graduate job, such as its location or the likely working hours.

Across the full survey sample, final year students named more than 1,500 different organisations,

> **" The accounting & professional services firm PwC is back at the top of the rankings for the first time since 2018. "**

THE TIMES TOP 100 GRADUATE EMPLOYERS
The Times Top 100 Graduate Employers 2023

	2022			2022	
1	3	PWC	51	NEW	DLA PIPER
2	1	CIVIL SERVICE	52	50	VODAFONE
3	2	NHS	53	26	ACCENTURE
4	4	DELOITTE	54	54	BAIN & COMPANY
5	5	GOOGLE	55	55	TESCO
6	6	EY	56	70	JANE STREET
7	7	BBC	57	73	LOCAL GOVERNMENT
8	8	KPMG	58	91	CLYDE & CO
9	9	ALDI	59	63	JAGUAR LAND ROVER
10	15	BARCLAYS	60	42	BLOOMBERG
11	12	J.P. MORGAN	61	72	SANTANDER
12	10	AMAZON	62	NEW	AECOM
13	16	HSBC	63	43	FRONTLINE
14	13	GSK	64	52	WHITE & CASE
15	14	TEACH FIRST	65	60	CMS
16	11	GOLDMAN SACHS	66	NEW	CHANNEL 4
17	17	CLIFFORD CHANCE	67	47	BT GROUP
18	18	MCKINSEY & COMPANY	68	51	BDO
19	19	L'ORÉAL	69	53	UBS
20	28	LLOYDS BANKING GROUP	70	57	DEUTSCHE BANK
21	20	UNILEVER	71	58	MCDONALD'S
22	67	UNLOCKED GRADUATES	72	95	HOGAN LOVELLS
23	21	LINKLATERS	73	NEW	MARKS & SPENCER
24	32	NEWTON	74	59	MI5 - THE SECURITY SERVICE
25	22	ASTRAZENECA	75	61	BANK OF AMERICA
26	34	LIDL	76	68	SAVILLS
27	37	APPLE	77	74	BAKER MCKENZIE
28	25	BAE SYSTEMS	78	NEW	SIEMENS
29	24	ARUP	79	49	BLACKROCK
30	44	MICROSOFT	80	76	SHELL
31	39	PROCTER & GAMBLE	81	62	BANK OF ENGLAND
32	29	MORGAN STANLEY	82	82	AON
33	30	BCG	83	NEW	BRITISH AIRWAYS
34	23	ROLLS-ROYCE	84	98	MOTT MACDONALD
35	33	ALLEN & OVERY	85	89	KUBRICK
36	35	NATWEST GROUP	86	90	LATHAM & WATKINS
37	36	SLAUGHTER AND MAY	87	NEW	JOHNSON & JOHNSON
38	45	IBM	88	NEW	MERCEDES
39	46	PENGUIN	89	41	CITI
40	40	BP	90	96	GRANT THORNTON
41	27	SKY	91	NEW	CANCER RESEARCH UK
42	75	AIRBUS	92	NEW	SECRET INTELLIGENCE SERVICE (MI6)
43	38	POLICE NOW	93	NEW	JACOBS
44	88	FRESHFIELDS	94	NEW	MAZARS
45	56	HERBERT SMITH FREEHILLS	95	77	ARCADIS
46	48	ATKINS	96	80	MARS
47	31	BRITISH ARMY	97	99	ENTERPRISE
48	64	ROYAL NAVY	98	NEW	CAPGEMINI
49	69	PFIZER	99	NEW	WSP
50	71	DYSON	100	NEW	AVIVA

Source **High Fliers Research** 13,309 final year students leaving UK universities in the summer of 2023 were asked the open-ended question "Which employer do you think offers the best opportunities for graduates?" during interviews for *The UK Graduate Careers Survey 2023* from well-known national and international organisations to small and medium-sized regional and local employers. The responses were analysed and the one hundred organisations that were named most often make up *The Times Top 100 Graduate Employers* for 2023.

In a dramatic twist, the accounting & professional services firm PwC has been voted the UK's leading graduate employer, taking the firm back to the top of the rankings for the first time since 2018. In a very close result, 5.4 per cent of final year students from the 'Class of 2023' voted for the firm.

The Civil Service, best-known for its prestigious Fast Stream programme, moved down into second place, after four years as the country's number one graduate employer. And having reaching its highest-ever position in 2022, the NHS has also moved down, to third place this year.

Deloitte, the second of the 'Big Four' accounting & professional services firms is unchanged in fourth place, as are rivals EY and KPMG in sixth and eighth places respectively. Technology giant Google remains in fifth place and there is no change for either the BBC or retailer Aldi. Banking giant Barclays has overtaken HSBC, J.P. Morgan and Goldman Sachs to reach the top ten for the first time.

Amazon has slipped back to 12th place this year. The widely-respected Teach First programme is in 15th place but Goldman Sachs drops five places to 16th. Law firm Clifford Chance, management consultants McKinsey & Company and L'Oréal, the consumer goods company, each continue in their highest-ever positions, whilst the Lloyds Banking Group has secured a place in the top twenty for the first time.

Within the new *Top 100*, the year's highest climbers are led by the Unlocked Graduates prison officer programme which has leapt a very impressive forty-five places to 22nd place, up from 67th place in 2022. Law firm Freshfields has had a similar rise, jumping forty-four places to 44th place, and aerospace manufacturer Airbus and Clyde & Co have both climbed more than thirty places in this year's *Top 100*.

Citi has had the most significant fall of the year, dropping forty-eight places from 41st place in 2022 to 89th place, and is one of seven investment banks or asset managers that have been ranked lower this year. Technology company Accenture has fallen twenty-seven places to 53rd place, its lowest-ever ranking. The Frontline graduate

programme and BT have each dropped twenty places in the new rankings.

There are fifteen new entries or re-entries in this year's *Top 100*, making this the second-biggest changeover of ranked employers in the history of *The Times Top 100 Graduate Employers*. The highest are law firm DLA Piper, which returns in 51st place, and engineering consultants AECOM which reappears in 62nd place.

There are a further seven *Top 100* re-entries, for Channel 4, Marks & Spencer, British Airways, industrial manufacturer Siemens, pharmaceuticals company Johnson & Johnson, charity Cancer Research UK and technology company Capgemini, which is back in the rankings for the first time in sixteen years.

They are joined by car company Mercedes, the Secret Intelligence Service (MI6), professional services firm Mazars, engineering & technical consulting firms Jacobs and WSP, and insurance company Aviva – each of which are ranked for the first time.

Among the graduate employers leaving the *Top 100* in 2023 are Think Ahead, the mental health graduate programme – and GCHQ, the Government intelligence, cyber and security agency which is unranked for the first time in five years.

Other graduate employers that have left this year's league table include law firm Irwin Mitchell, retailer THG, investment bank Credit Suisse and technology company TPP, with a further seven graduate employers that were new or re-entries in the 2022 rankings – Specsavers, social media favourites TikTok, Cardiff-headquartered law firm Hugh James, PA Consulting, PepsiCo, Reed Smith and American Express.

Since the original edition of *The Times Top 100 Graduate Employers* was published two and a half decades ago, just three organisations have made it to number one in the rankings.

Andersen Consulting (now Accenture) held on to the top spot for the first four years, beginning in 1999, and its success heralded a huge surge in popularity for careers in consulting. At its peak in 2001, almost one in six graduates applied for jobs in the sector.

In the year before the firm changed its name from Andersen Consulting to Accenture, it astutely introduced a new graduate package that included a £28,500 starting salary (a sky-high figure for graduates in 2000) and a much-talked-

ICAEW

Claris Jekwa ACA,
Contribution Margin Controller, BMW

"I'm given responsibility.
It's empowering."

ACCOUNTANCY WILL
GET YOU THERE.

From influencing the latest online trend,
to charity work across the country,
it's time to expect the unexpected with
a qualification that will put you in the
driver's seat. Whatever your degree,
see yourself in accountancy with an
ICAEW qualification.

Accountancy can take you anywhere.

icaew.com/careers

about £10,000 bonus, helping to assure the firm's popularity, irrespective of its corporate branding.

In 2003, after two dismal years in graduate recruitment when vacancies for university-leavers dropped by more than a fifth following the 9/11 terrorist attacks in 2001, the Civil Service was named the UK's leading graduate employer.

Just twelve months later it was displaced by PricewaterhouseCoopers, the accounting and professional services firm formed from the merger of Price Waterhouse and Coopers & Lybrand in 1998. At the time, the firm was the largest private sector recruiter of graduates, with an intake in 2004 of more than a thousand trainees.

Now known simply as PwC, the firm remained at number one for an impressive fifteen years, increasing its share of the student vote from 5 per cent in 2004 to more than 10 per cent in 2007, and fighting off the stiffest of competition from rivals Deloitte in 2008, when just seven votes separated the two employers.

PwC's reign as the UK's leading graduate employer represented a real renaissance for the entire accounting & professional services sector.

Twenty years ago, a career in accountancy was often regarded as a safe, traditional employment choice, whereas today's profession is viewed in a very different light. The training required to become a chartered accountant is now seen as a prized business qualification, and the sector's leading firms are regularly described as 'dynamic' and 'international' by undergraduates looking for their first job after university – and continue to dominate the annual graduate employer rankings.

A total of 237 different organisations have now appeared within *The Times Top 100 Graduate Employers* since its inception, and thirty-six of these graduate employers hold the inspiring record of being ranked within the *Top 100* in all twenty-five editions since 1999.

The most consistent performers have been PwC, KPMG and the Civil Service, each of which have never been lower than 10th place in the league table. The NHS has also had a formidable record, appearing in every top ten since 2003, while the BBC and EY (formerly Ernst & Young) have both remained within the top twenty throughout the past twenty-five years. And consumer goods

THE TIMES TOP 100 GRADUATE EMPLOYERS
Number Ones, Movers & Shakers in the Top 100

NUMBER ONES		HIGHEST CLIMBING EMPLOYERS		HIGHEST NEW ENTRIES	
1999	ANDERSEN CONSULTING	1999	SCHLUMBERGER (UP 13 PLACES)	1999	PFIZER (31st)
2000	ANDERSEN CONSULTING	2000	CAPITAL ONE (UP 32 PLACES)	2000	MORGAN STANLEY (34th)
2001	ACCENTURE	2001	EUROPEAN COMMISSION (UP 36 PLACES)	2001	MARCONI (36th)
2002	ACCENTURE	2002	WPP (UP 36 PLACES)	2002	GUINNESS UDV (44th)
2003	CIVIL SERVICE	2003	ROLLS-ROYCE (UP 37 PLACES)	2003	ASDA (40th)
2004	PRICEWATERHOUSECOOPERS	2004	J.P. MORGAN (UP 29 PLACES)	2004	BAKER & MCKENZIE (61st)
2005	PRICEWATERHOUSECOOPERS	2005	TEACH FIRST (UP 22 PLACES)	2005	PENGUIN (70th)
2006	PRICEWATERHOUSECOOPERS	2006	GOOGLE (UP 32 PLACES)	2006	FUJITSU (81st)
2007	PRICEWATERHOUSECOOPERS	2007	PFIZER (UP 30 PLACES)	2007	BDO STOY HAYWARD (74th)
2008	PRICEWATERHOUSECOOPERS	2008	CO-OPERATIVE GROUP (UP 39 PLACES)	2008	SKY (76th)
2009	PRICEWATERHOUSECOOPERS	2009	CADBURY (UP 48 PLACES)	2009	BDO STOY HAYWARD (68th)
2010	PRICEWATERHOUSECOOPERS	2010	ASDA (UP 41 PLACES)	2010	SAATCHI & SAATCHI (49th)
2011	PWC	2011	CENTRICA (UP 41 PLACES)	2011	APPLE (53rd)
2012	PWC	2012	NESTLÉ (UP 44 PLACES)	2012	EUROPEAN COMMISSION (56th)
2013	PWC	2013	DFID (UP 40 PLACES)	2013	SIEMENS (70th)
2014	PWC	2014	TRANSPORT FOR LONDON (UP 36 PLACES)	2014	FRONTLINE (76th)
2015	PWC	2015	DIAGEO, NEWTON (UP 43 PLACES)	2015	DANONE (66th)
2016	PWC	2016	BANK OF ENGLAND (UP 34 PLACES)	2016	SANTANDER (63rd)
2017	PWC	2017	CANCER RESEARCH UK (UP 38 PLACES)	2017	DYSON (52nd)
2018	PWC	2018	MCDONALD'S (UP 30 PLACES)	2018	ASOS (52nd)
2019	CIVIL SERVICE	2019	POLICE NOW (UP 43 PLACES)	2019	UNLOCKED (49th)
2020	CIVIL SERVICE	2020	DLA PIPER WHITE & CASE (UP 32 PLACES)	2020	CHANNEL FOUR (77th)
2021	CIVIL SERVICE	2021	CHARITYWORKS (UP 45 PLACES)	2021	BDO (49th)
2022	CIVIL SERVICE	2022	JAGUAR LAND ROVER (UP 30 PLACES)	2022	BMW GROUP (66th)
2023	PWC	2023	UNLOCKED (UP 45 PLACES)	2023	DLA PIPER (51st)

Source High Fliers Research

company Unilever and investment bank Goldman Sachs are two more employers have have appeared in the top quarter of the rankings each year.

Google is the highest-climbing employer within the *Top 100,* having risen over eighty places during its first decade in the rankings, to reach the top three for the first time in 2015. But car manufacturer Jaguar Land Rover holds the record for the fastest-moving employer, after jumping more than seventy places in just five years, between 2009 and 2014.

Other well-known graduate employers haven't been so successful. British Airways ranked in 6th place in 1999 but dropped out of the *Top 100* a decade later, and Ford, which was once rated as high as 14th, disappeared out of the list in 2006 after cancelling its graduate recruitment programme two years previously.

More recent high-ranking casualties include the John Lewis Partnership which – having been

9th in 2003 – tumbled out of the *Top 100* in 2020 and Boots, the pharmacy and health retailer that initially appeared in 10th place in the first edition of *The Times Top 100 Graduate Employers* disappeared from the rankings in 2021. ExxonMobil, the oil & energy company that was a top twenty employer in the original *Top 100*, has aso been unranked since 2021. And Marks & Spencer which was in 7th place in the inaugural *Top 100* in 1999, dropped out of the rankings altogether in 2022.

More than thirty graduate employers – including Nokia, Maersk, the Home Office, Cable & Wireless, United Biscuits, Nationwide, Capgemini and the Met Office – have the dubious record of having only been ranked in the *Top 100* once during the last twenty years. And former engineering & telecommunications company Marconi had the unusual distinction of being one of the highest-ever new entries, in 36th place in 2001, only to vanish from the list entirely the following year.

THE TIMES TOP 100 — Winners & Losers in the Top 100

EMPLOYERS CLIMBING HIGHEST	HIGHEST RANKING	LOWEST RANKING
TESCO	100th (1999)	12th (2012)
GOOGLE	85th (2005)	3rd (2015)
LIDL	89th (2009)	13th (2017)
NEWTON	94th (2013)	19th (2019)
AMAZON	81st (2015)	10th (2022)
JAGUAR LAND ROVER	87th (2009)	16th (2014)
ALDI	65th (2002)	2nd (2015-2016)
MI5 – THE SECURITY SERVICE	96th (2007)	33rd (2010)
POLICE NOW	90th (2018)	28th (2021)
TEACH FIRST	63rd (2003)	2nd (2014)
APPLE	87th (2009)	27th (2012)
DEUTSCHE BANK	81st (1999)	23rd (2005)
ATKINS	94th (2004)	37th (2009)
SLAUGHTER AND MAY	90th (2001)	36th (2022)
FRONTLINE	76th (2014)	26th (2018)
EMPLOYERS FALLING FURTHEST	**HIGHEST RANKING**	**LOWEST RANKING**
BRITISH AIRWAYS	6th (1999)	Not ranked (2010, 2011, 2017, 2019-2022)
MARKS & SPENCER	7th (1999)	Not ranked (2021-2022)
JOHN LEWIS PARTNERSHIP	9th (2013)	Not ranked (FROM 2020)
BOOTS	10th (1999)	Not ranked (FROM 2021)
FORD	11th (1999)	Not ranked (FROM 2006)
UBS	17th (2002)	Not ranked (2018)
SAINSBURY'S	18th (2003)	Not ranked (FROM 2016)
EXXONMOBIL	19th (1999)	Not ranked (FROM 2021)
SHELL	11th (2006)	90th (2021)
THOMSON REUTERS	22nd (2001)	Not ranked (2009-2012, FROM 2014)
BANK OF AMERICA	27th (2000)	Not ranked (FROM 2017-2020)
ASDA	27th (2004)	Not ranked (FROM 2018)
RAF	32nd (2005)	Not ranked (2015, FROM 2021)
SCHRODERS	35th (1999)	Not ranked (FROM 2002)
MINISTRY OF DEFENCE	35th (2003)	Not ranked (2007, FROM 2012)

Source High Fliers Research

With ICAS, opportunity doesn't knock. It kicks down the door.

Learn more about how a Chartered Accountancy qualification with ICAS can fast-track your ambitions.

With ICAS, a career in Chartered Accountancy means open access to a whole world of possibilities – so there's no end to where your career could take you.

icas.com/ opportunitykicks

One of the most spectacular ascendancies in the *Top 100* has been the rise of Aldi, which joined the list in 65th place in 2002, rose to 3rd place in 2009 – helped in part by its memorable remuneration package for new recruits (currently £50,000 plus a fully-expensed VW electric car) – and was ranked in 2nd place in both 2015 and 2016. Consulting firm Newton is another impressive climber, having jumped more than seventy places from 94th place in 2013 to being ranked in the top twenty for the first time in 2019.

Teach First, the first of five inspirational schemes that are transforming society by bringing top graduates into public service, appeared as a new entry in 63rd place in 2003, before climbing the rankings every year for a decade and reaching 2nd place in the *Top 100* in 2014. Frontline, the children's social work graduate programme, was a new entry in 76th place that year, before progressing fifty places to 26th place by 2018. And over the past five years another of these programmes, Police Now, has jumped more than sixty places from 90th in 2018 to 28th place in the 2021 rankings.

Together, the twenty-five annual editions of *The Times Top 100 Graduates Employers* have produced a definitive record of the graduate employers that generations of students and recent graduates have aspired to join after leaving university – and these latest results provide a unique insight into how the 'Class of 2023' rated the country's leading graduate employers.

THE TIMES TOP 100 GRADUATE EMPLOYERS
Employers Ranked for 25 Years in the Top 100

MOST CONSISTENT EMPLOYERS	HIGHEST RANKING	LOWEST RANKING
PWC	1st (2004-2018, 2023)	3rd (1999-2001, 2003, 2022)
CIVIL SERVICE	1st (2003, 2019-2022)	8th (2011)
KPMG	3rd (2006-2008, 2011-2012)	10th (2021)
BBC	5th (2005-2007)	14th (1999)
GSK	10th (2017-2018)	22nd (2002-2003)
EY (FORMERLY ERNST & YOUNG)	6th (2021-2023)	20th (2001)
GOLDMAN SACHS	5th (2001)	25th (1999)
HSBC	6th (2003)	29th (1999)
NHS	2nd (2022)	27th (1999, 2002)
BARCLAYS	10th (2023)	35th (2006)
UNILEVER	7th (2002)	23rd (2008)
BAE SYSTEMS	23rd (1999)	49th (2015)
DELOITTE	2nd (2013)	30th (2001)
BP	14th (2003-2004)	42th (2021)
CLIFFORD CHANCE	17th (2022-2023)	45th (2007, 2012)
McKINSEY & COMPANY	18th (2022-2023)	48th (2008)
IBM	13th (2000)	46th (2022)
ALLEN & OVERY	24th (2010)	57th (2005)
PROCTER & GAMBLE	4th (1999-2001)	39th (2022)
J.P.MORGAN	10th (2019-2020)	45th (2003)
LLOYDS BANKING GROUP	20th (2023)	56th (2001)
ARUP	24th (2021-2022)	60th (2001)
MICROSOFT	21st (2004-2005)	58th (1999)
LINKLATERS	19th (2021)	59th (2000)
BRITISH ARMY	4th (2003)	47rd (2023)
ACCENTURE	1st (1999-2002)	53rd (2023)
ROLLS-ROYCE	15th (2019)	68th (2002)
ROYAL NAVY	35th (2010)	88th (2013)
BT	14th (2000)	72nd (2010)
CITI	30th (2008)	89th (2023)
DEUTSCHE BANK	23rd (2005)	88th (2018)
L'ORÉAL	19th (2022-2023)	85th (2018)
McDONALD'S	29th (2003)	98th (2016-2017)
SHELL	11th (2006)	90th (2021)
MARS	9th (2000)	96th (2023)
TESCO	12th (2012)	100th (1999)

Source High Fliers Research

Deloitte.

Choose Your Impact

Whichever programme you join, you'll get to know all kinds of amazing people to make positive change happen together. To inspiring colleagues in the UK and around the world. To a purpose that's shared, and that you can meaningfully contribute to. To work that challenges, and progress that never stops. To possibilities and projects in industries you may never have experienced before. And to opportunities to make a collaborative impact that reaches further and means more.

Find a career with endless opportunities to make an impact at **deloitte.co.uk/earlycareers**

Civil Service
Fast Stream

Grow like nowhere else

BOOST
YOUR
KNOWLEDGE

SHAPE NATIONWIDE CHANGE

Graduate Leadership and Management Development Programme
Nationwide Opportunities

Go further, sooner. Own your development on our unique, career-accelerating programme. And put what you learn into practice, on work that impacts our nation.

Join the Fast Stream and grow the skills, knowledge and networks you'll need to advance your career progression to the most senior levels of the Civil Service.

We offer 15 different professional schemes. Each one offers high-quality practical training, on-the-job learning, a breadth of experience across a range of postings, and a career path in a government profession.

Whichever scheme you join you'll help drive forward government operational services, and policies that make meaningful change for millions of people. From clean energy, cybersecurity and defence, to health, housing, international relations and more, you could help tackle some of our biggest challenges.

We're here to develop future leaders and managers, building a Civil Service that represents every community and keeps ahead in our fast-changing world. We want science and engineering to be at the heart of government decision making. So – while we welcome graduates from all backgrounds – if you have a STEM degree, we're keen to hear from you.

faststream.gov.uk

University graduates want starting salaries of £30,000

University strikes have stolen my degree and future prospects

ANNA MCGOVERN

PM VOWS TO CURB 'RIP-OFF' DEGREES

UNIVERSITIES offering 'rip-off' courses will be subject to strict controls to...

By Harriet Line
Deputy Political Editor

ready for valuable careers', it is not the case everywhere.

'There are too many universities offering poor courses that...

and poor employment prospects

Students' anger as they're told they can't graduate due to strike

Strong wage growth underlines inflation fears

DELPHINE STRAUSS
ECONOMICS CORRESPONDENT

cooling were becoming clearer and could "ease some of the MPC's angst over persistent inflation".

Yesterday's figures suggested that high inflation and rising interest rates were starting to weigh on hiring. The unemployment rate increased 0.1 percentage points to 3.9 per cent as people who had previously chosen not to look for work returned to job-seeking.

The rate of economic inactivity fell percentage points from the previous three months, to 21 per cent, largely

Jobs market remains tough for graduate

GRADUATES leaving university will find it more difficult to get work even though job vacancies and advertised salaries the wider economy continued to increase in May, according to a new report.

Jobs site Adzuna said that despite rising vacancy numbers and salaries across the board graduate roles are down by 11% since 2022 and are taking around 40 days to fill on average – the longest of any other

Universities whose alumni earn £40k on graduation

Students have lost out to fee increases pandemic lockdowns and lecturer strikes but a university degree can still be a golden ticket to a well-paid job – you study at the right place, that is.

Indeed, graduates from a select group of British universities now earn around £40,000 or more on average in the first five years after finishing their studies, research has revealed.

The average salary for jobs requiring a university degree is no...

Lockdowns and recession will blight careers of graduates

By Szu Ping Chan

COVID lockdowns and a looming recession...

dence that the pandemic had left pupils behind on reading.

Other studies show people...

degree online, with few internship opportunities, and will enter a labour recession with less academic experience". Someone born in had have spent the last three secondary school in the pandemic, simulating learning losses, have education in 2023 in the recession".

demic and lockdowns have a widespread deterioration health, with young people the most, according to

UK graduates repaying loans rises to 2.5mn

GRADUATE FINANCE
Total student loan book reaches more than £200bn

RAFE UDDIN
Thousands more UK graduates are paying back student loans after the government last year froze the income threshold at which payments start, in advance of a further squeeze on new students this autumn.

Data published by the Student Loan Company on Thursday, showed that the number of students making repayments leapt to 2.5mn, representing a 13 per cent increase

Labour has pledged to lower monthly student loan repayments if elected, but has yet to set out how it would implement proposals it claimed wouldn't affect government borrowing.

SLC said that on average English students graduated with debt around £45 figure consistent with the previous two years. A person average levels of debt need to earn £62,795 more to repay the amount accrued on their loan period, said the IFS.

Analysis by the th showed that a sharp in the maximum charged on student

March and 7.1 per cent from May, a rate fixed until August.

Ogden added that frozen repayment thresholds meant individuals earning over the ...more...

above a set threshold, depending on when they completed their undergraduate degree. Separate thresholds exist for postgraduate loans and in the nations.

£542mn in 2022-23. The current loan structure means only those likely to pay back the loan in full benefit from such contributions.

It does make sense for

loans and they will be written off," said Brian Byrnes, head of personal finance at investment app Moneybox.

The Department for Education said: "Student loans pro-keepers and ensure

PwC was right to scrap 2:1 degrees for hires - next they should ditch all academic marks

EARLIER this week, PwC announced that graduates would no longer need a 2:1 degree in order to...

Khyati Sundaram

marginalised backgrounds are less likely to have had optimal environ-their education - especially it being relegated to the Disadvantaged students likely to attend university place.

have said that they want to representation of black and people amongst their

is the most accurate way of predicting performance. It also shows that when all candidates are given a fair chance and we test true talent, diversity follows organically.

Following a study by Applied which looked at 1,300 candidates hired in financial services and consulting roles, we found that firms that swapped CVs for anonymous applic...

Britain's double-digit inflation problem

Price growth should soon, but the Bank of England still has wor

Britain's economy has been number of reasons recently expects UK growth to b among large economies th also suffered the bigges workforce participation nation since the pand

Fewer graduate employers demand a 2:1

Nicola Woolcock Education Editor

Fewer than half of graduate employers asked recruits for a 2:1 degree this year, for the first time.

Leading companies are keen to diversify their intake and some are running applications that are "blind" to the applicant's name, university or even degree classification.

Most graduates now achieve a 2:1 or a first, meaning it is harder for employers to use this as a way of choosing candidates. A report published yesterday by

Analysis

How are employers recruiting now? Companies often use aptitude and behaviour tests (Nicola Woolcock writes). These can include games that measure skills and abilities. Some ask candidates to send video interviews rather than covering letters. Others require applicants

and the figure now stands at 26 per cent. PwC, the consultancy firm, said this year that it was removing the 2:1 criteria for graduate roles to ensure it does not miss out on talent. It added: "More students will be able to access PwC's programmes as the firm assesses potential instead of academic attainment."

The survey of 168 companies, taking on 32,000 employees, found recruitment was up 19 per cent on last year and the average graduate salary was almost £31,000, compared with nearly £20,000 for school and college leavers. Grad

Firms received on average 36 applications per vacancy, a significant decrease from 91 last year, which suggests graduates are being more selective.

Digital and IT was the most competitive sector, with 90 applications per vacancy on average, while energy and engineering and the legal sector were the least competitive, with an average of 47 applications per vacancy.

Forty-seven per cent of the graduate cohort was female, even though 57 per cent of university students are women,

want to broaden their potential talent pool. The shift also reflects the lower application to vacancy ratio in 2022, and the increased difficulty with filling vacancies this year.

Nick Hillman, director of the Higher Education Policy Institute, said: "Clearly, when the overwhelming majority of undergraduates emerge with what used to be called a '2:1 degree', then their grades become a less useful differentiator. It is hard for employers to know if a 2:1 from an institution that

Understanding the Graduate Job Market

By Martin Birchall
Managing Director, High Fliers Research

In the two and a half decades since the first edition of *The Times Top 100 Graduate Employers* was published in 1999, graduate recruitment at the UK's leading employers has increased very substantially.

The number of graduate vacancies on offer to university-leavers has increased in seventeen of the past twenty-five years and reached a new record level in 2023, with almost twice as many opportunities available, compared to graduate recruitment at the end of the 1990s.

But this sustained period of growth in graduate jobs has been punctuated by four significant downturns in recruitment.

In the two years following the 9/11 terrorist attacks in the US, the worsening economic outlook prompted employers in the UK to reduce their entry-level vacancies for new graduates by more than 15 per cent.

Graduate recruitment recovered in 2004 and vacancies for university-leavers grew at between 10 and 12 per cent annually over the next three years, before the global financial crisis of 2008 and 2009 heralded the worst recession in the UK since the Second World War.

Graduate vacancies at the country's top employers plunged by an unprecedented 23 per cent in less than 18 months – and almost 10,000 jobs were cut or left unfilled from a planned intake of more than 40,000 new graduates during this period. A record fifty-nine of the employers featured in *The Times Top 100 Graduate Employers* reduced their graduate hiring in 2009 alone.

Although the graduate job market bounced back successfully in 2010, with an annual increase in vacancies of more than 12 per cent, it took a further five years for graduate recruitment to return to the pre-recession peak recorded in 2007.

The uncertainty that followed Britain's vote to leave the European Union in 2016 saw graduate vacancies dip again in 2017. But growth returned a year later and by 2019 entry-level recruitment was up by 43 per cent compared to the number of vacancies available in 2009 – the low point in graduate recruitment during the economic crisis – and had been expected to rise even higher in 2020.

But the start of the Coronavirus pandemic in March 2020 forced the UK's top employers to pause or re-evaluate their graduate recruitment and many were unable to continue with that year's planned annual intake of university-leavers.

Graduate recruitment was cut in thirteen out of fifteen industries and business sectors, most noticeably at major engineering & industrial companies and accounting & professional services firms, where over 700 planned vacancies were left unfilled. The final number of graduates recruited

> *The number of graduate jobs on offer to university-leavers has increased in seventeen of the past twenty-five years.*

It's a fantastic opportunity to develop as a person, as a professional and as a leader.

With Unlocked Graduates, I was put in positions very early on where I had to organise a team. I learned to lead the people I was looking after in that environment and learned so many skills in working with different personalities as well as managing expectations and challenges. Following my two years on the Unlocked programme, I now work as a Senior Policy Advisor for the Civil Service.

Unlocked
unlockedgrads.org.uk

by employers featured in *The Times Top 100 Graduate Employers* in 2020 was 12 per cent lower than in 2019.

Recruitment began to bounce back in 2021 with a substantial 9.4 per cent rise in entry-level vacancies – the 'V-shaped' pandemic recovery in the graduate job market largely mirroring the recovery in the wider economy.

This strong growth gathered pace the following year when graduate vacancies increased in all fifteen industries and business sectors represented in *The Times Top 100 Graduate Employers*. In all, the number of graduate jobs available jumped by 14.5 per cent in 2022, the largest-ever year-on-year rise in graduate recruitment at the UK's leading employers.

During 2023, although the growth in graduate vacancies slowed, recruitment increased by a further 6.3 per cent, taking the number of graduate opportunities for university-leavers to a new all-time high.

At the beginning of the new 2023-2024 recruitment season, the employers listed in *The Times Top 100 Graduate Employers* are predicting that they will have a total of 28,948 graduate vacancies for autumn 2024 start dates.

Although this is 3.3 per cent fewer than the record number of new graduates recruited in 2023, recruitment at the country's most sought-after graduate employers remains at its second-highest level ever.

A quarter of employers are planning to hire more graduates in 2024, two fifths expect to match their previous intake, but almost a third of organisations are likely to recruit fewer university-leavers over the coming year.

The country's leading accounting & professional services firms recruited an unprecedented number of university-leavers in 2023 – a total of more than 7,000 trainees. Although this year's recruitment targets are a little lower, the sector is expected to be the largest recruiter of new graduates in 2024.

Graduate vacancies in the public sector are expected to increase for the third consecutive year, with more than 4,500 entry level opportunities available. But following a noticeable rise in recruitment at engineering & industrial companies in 2023, these employers are set to reduce their graduate intake in 2024.

Whilst there are expected to be fewer graduate vacancies at the City's investment banks and fund managers, employers elsewhere in the banking

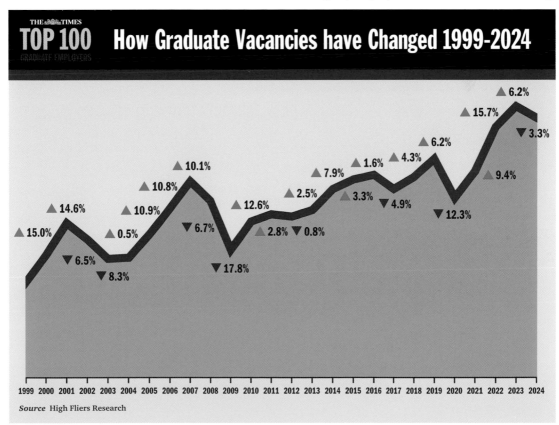

THE TIMES TOP 100 GRADUATE EMPLOYERS

How Graduate Vacancies have Changed 1999-2024

Source High Fliers Research

and finance sector anticipate a sharp increase in their 2024 graduate intake – an annual rise in vacancies of almost a third.

Overall, graduate recruitment is predicted to rise or match 2023 recruitment levels in eight out of fifteen key industries and business sectors in the next 12 months, but in the remaining seven sectors, graduate vacancies are expected to decrease.

The two employers from *The Times Top 100 Graduate Employers* with the biggest graduate recruitment targets for 2024 are the accounting & professional services firm PwC – which is aiming to recruit 1,800 new trainees in the year ahead – and Teach First, the popular programme that recruits

new graduates to teach in schools in low-income communities around the UK, has 1,750 places available.

Other very substantial individual graduate recruiters in 2024 include the car & van rental company Enterprise (1,600 graduate vacancies), Deloitte (1,500 vacancies), technology company Accenture, the Civil Service Fast Stream and accounting & professional services firms EY and KPMG (1,000 vacancies each).

More than three-fifths of *Top 100* employers have vacancies for graduates in technology, over half have opportunities in finance, and a third are recruiting for sales and marketing jobs, human

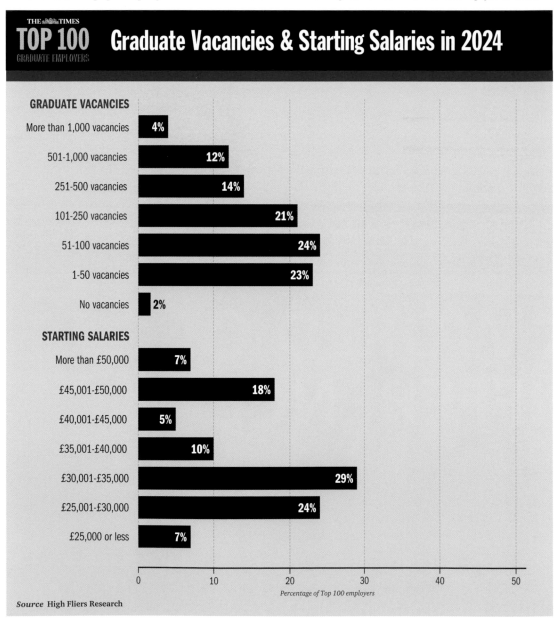

TOP 100 Graduate Vacancies & Starting Salaries in 2024

GRADUATE EMPLOYERS

GRADUATE VACANCIES

More than 1,000 vacancies	4%
501-1,000 vacancies	12%
251-500 vacancies	14%
101-250 vacancies	21%
51-100 vacancies	24%
1-50 vacancies	23%
No vacancies	2%

STARTING SALARIES

More than £50,000	7%
£45,001-£50,000	18%
£40,001-£45,000	5%
£35,001-£40,000	10%
£30,001-£35,000	29%
£25,001-£30,000	24%
£25,000 or less	7%

Percentage of Top 100 employers

Source **High Fliers Research**

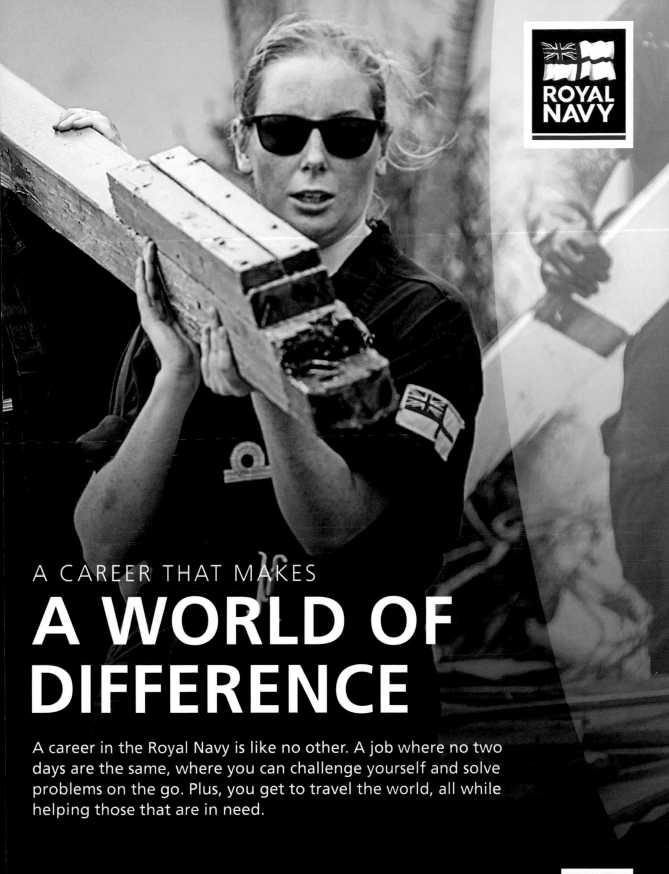

A CAREER THAT MAKES
A WORLD OF DIFFERENCE

A career in the Royal Navy is like no other. A job where no two days are the same, where you can challenge yourself and solve problems on the go. Plus, you get to travel the world, all while helping those that are in need.

For more information call 0345 607 5555
Visit royalnavy.mod.uk/careers

resources roles, engineering positions, or general management vacancies.

A fifth of the country's top graduate employers are looking for new recruits to work in research & development, but there are fewer graduate jobs available in retailing or in more specialist areas, such as purchasing, logistics & supply chain, property and the media.

Over three-quarters of *Top 100* employers have graduate vacancies in London in 2024, and half have posts available elsewhere in the south east of England. Up to half also have roles in the north west of England, the south west, the Midlands, Yorkshire and the north east. Two-fifths are recruiting for graduate roles in Scotland, but Northern Ireland, Wales and East Anglia have the fewest employers with vacancies this year.

Graduate starting salaries at the UK's leading employers changed little between 2012 and 2021, increasing by just £1,000 in this nine-year period to a median of £30,000. But this rose to £32,000 in 2022 – the first annual boost in starting salaries for seven years – and went up again in 2023 to a new median of £33,500.

These rates are expected to increase further in 2024, with the most generous starting salaries available at the leading investment banks & fund managers (a median of £55,000), law firms (£50,000) and consulting firms (£47,500).

A quarter of employers featured in *The Times Top 100 Graduate Employers* are now offering starting salaries in excess of £45,000 for their new recruits. The most generous salaries publicised within this edition are at the law firm White & Case, which is offering new trainees a salary of £52,000 in 2024. Rival firms Clifford Chance, Slaughter and May Freshfields, Latham & Watkins and Linklaters each have graduate starting salaries of £50,000.

Consulting firm Newton also offers graduate packages worth up to £50,000, whilst retailer Aldi continues to pay a sector-leading graduate starting salary for its Area Management trainee programme, which has been increased to £50,000 for 2024.

Half of the UK's leading employers now recruit graduates year-round, or in different phases during the year, and will accept applications throughout the 2023-2024 recruitment season until all their vacancies are filled. For employers with an annual application deadline, most are in November or December, although a limited number have October or post-Christmas deadlines for their graduate programmes.

This means that there is every incentive to apply early for the near-record number of graduate vacancies that are available in 2024 at the employers featured in *The Times Top 100 Graduate Employers*.

THE TIMES TOP 100 GRADUATE EMPLOYERS — Graduate Vacancies at Top 100 Employers in 2024

	2023		GRADUATE VACANCIES IN 2024	% CHANGE IN 2024	% CHANGE IN 2023	MEDIAN STARTING SALARY IN 2023
1.	1	ACCOUNTANCY & PROFESSIONAL SERVICES FIRMS	6,495	▼ 11.5%	▲ 6.0%	£35,000
2.	2	PUBLIC SECTOR EMPLOYERS	4,593	▲ 0.7%	▲ 11.3%	£27,700
3.	4	ENGINEERING & INDUSTRIAL COMPANIES	4,090	▼ 5.1%	▲ 33.7%	£30,000
4.	3	TECHNOLOGY COMPANIES	3,220	▼ 6.0%	NO CHANGE	£33,500
5.	7	BANKING & FINANCIAL SERVICES	2,190	▲ 33.0%	▼ 9.6%	£40,000
6.	5	INVESTMENT BANKS & FUND MANAGERS	1,980	▼ 10.5%	▲ 2.6%	£55,000
7.	9	LAW FIRMS	1,237	▼ 0.9%	▼ 5.3%	£50,000
8.	8	ARMED FORCES	1,100	NO CHANGE	NO CHANGE	£28,900
9.	10	MEDIA ORGANISATIONS	782	▲ 7.0%	▼ 4.9%	£27,800
10.	6	RETAILERS	506	▼ 38.7%	▼ 3.6%	£32,000
11.	11	CONSULTING FIRMS	365	▲ 4.3%	▲ 3.7%	£47,500
12.	13	OIL & ENERGY COMPANIES	225	▼ 6.6%	▲ 56.5%	£35,000
13.	12	CONSUMER GOODS MANUFACTURERS	210	▲ 57.7%	NO CHANGE	£32,000
14.	15	CHEMICAL & PHARMACEUTICALS COMPANIES	205	▲ 32.9%	▲ 5.0%	£33,000
15.	-	CHARITIES & VOLUNTARY SECTOR	50	NO CHANGE	NO CHANGE	£25,000

Source High Fliers Research

Capgemini

ACHIEVE YOUR POTENTIAL

Rewrite your future.
Join Capgemini.
capgemini.com/careers

| GET THE FUTURE
YOU WANT

MORE REWARDS
Earn a market
leading salary
of **£50,000**
rising to **£90,615**

MORE BENEFITS
A fully expensed
electric car, five
weeks' holiday,
healthcare
and more

MORE
DEVELOPMENT
Learn through
our **12 month
training plan**
and dedicated
mentors

MORE
RESPONSIBILITY
Manage, coach
and lead a
**team of over
100 colleagues**

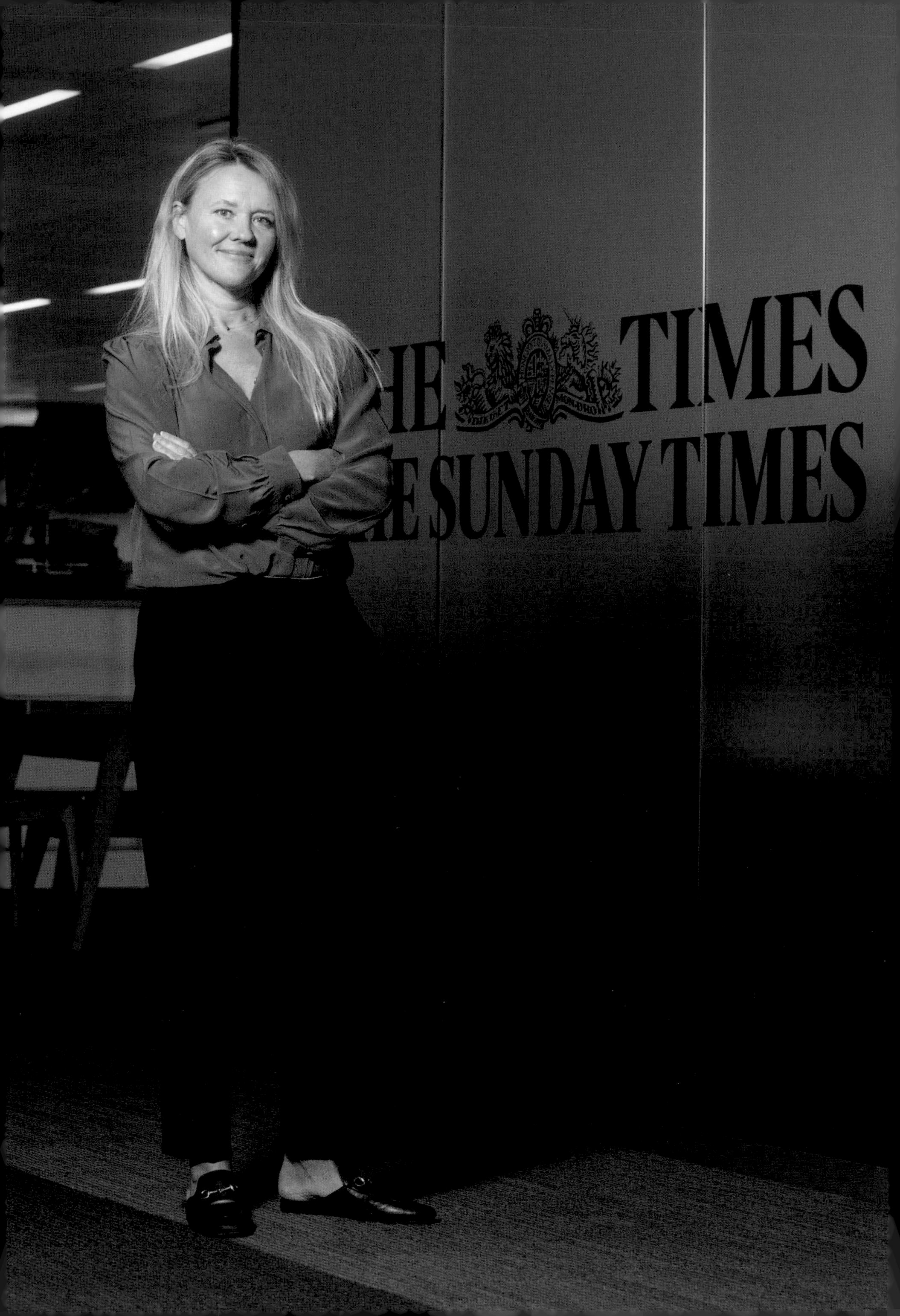
TIMES
SUNDAY TIMES

25 Years of Change for Universities, Students & Graduates

By **Zoe Thomas**
Author, *The Times & Sunday Times Good University Guide*

If you're one of more than 400,000 students preparing to leave university in the summer of 2024, then there's every chance that you weren't even born when our original league table of UK universities was published.

It was just before the turn of the millennium that *The Sunday Times* published its first dedicated *University Guide*. A 30-page print supplement, it came out in the autumn of 1998. The driving force behind our maiden edition was the introduction of £1,000 a year tuition fees that year. Paltry though this bill for university seems in comparison to the current £9,250 per year rate, what once was free had to be paid for – an educational choice became a financial one also. The same pound-shaped lens put graduate outcomes under the microscope – a university degree should offer new graduates a good return on their investment.

There were other huge shifts in higher education taking place at the time too – as numbers of students, and of universities, shot up. In 1999, the same year that the first edition of *The Times Top 100 Graduate Employers* was published, there were 98 universities in *The Sunday Times University Guide*. By 2009 there were 127 – reflecting the surge in former higher education colleges being awarded university status – among them Bath Spa, Worcester and Liverpool Hope – while others such as the University of the Arts London were created by the merger of a number of colleges. The decade before, in 1992, some 39 new universities had been created at a stroke, by the conversion of one-time polytechnics. The days of an academic elite drifting through hallowed halls clad in mortarboards and gowns was fading.

The sheer scale of expansion prompted a switch among universities from selecting undergraduates to recruiting them. Educationalists twenty-five years ago were shaking their heads and drawing the conclusion that degrees were being devalued.

The bold era of "education, education, education" under Tony Blair's New Labour government encompassed his pledge in 1999 for 50 per cent of young adults to go into higher education "in the next century".

In this diversifying higher education market, poorly advised school-leavers were at risk of having their decisions swayed by glossy university prospectuses or (a bit later) marketing ploys such as free laptops and cash bursary incentives.

Graduate numbers have soared in the past twenty years, figures tracked by the Higher Education Statistics Agency (HESA) show, rising from 237,000 in 1999 up to 308,395 in 2009 and first passing 400,000 in 2019. By 2022, a total of 408,300 graduates completed a full-time

" The average student debt for new graduates from the 'Class of 2023' was an eye-watering £43,000. "

**Graduate Management
Training Scheme**

Life-changing.
For you.
And potentially millions.

**When you work for the NHS, it's about making a difference.
Not just for you and your journey, but for millions of patients
and their families and communities.**

The NHS Graduate Management Training Scheme offers you a fast track to a senior
non-clinical role. It's your opportunity to get post-graduate qualifications, on-the-job
training and experience, early leadership responsibility and dedicated trainee support.
Not to mention building a supportive peer network with 249 other graduate trainees.

With placements across England in a variety of hospital and office settings, you could
be improving patient care, developing better ways to use data, creating new strategies
and much more.

**Your days will be challenging but exceptionally rewarding, and every day
you'll move towards becoming a healthcare leader of the future.**

THE TIMES
GRADUATE RECRUITMENT
AWARDS 2023
'Graduate Employer of Choice'
GENERAL MANAGEMENT

Start your journey here

undergraduate degree – a 72 per cent rise since 1999. Not even a global health pandemic dented the upturn, with limited opportunities to travel – or do anything else during Covid-19 – university proved an attractive choice, even by remote learning.

The Sunday Times University Guide – which merged with its sister publication *The Times Good University Guide* in 2014 – has from the outset evaluated the quality of what is available, giving facts, figures and comparative assessments of universities and courses. It has armed generations of students with the knowledge and insights to make informed choices.

Mirroring the burgeoning higher education landscape, our latest newspaper edition has more than tripled in pagination from its inaugural run, occupying 96 pages and featuring 134 universities. Our online edition features longer university profiles, more content and is fully searchable, while the *The Times & Sunday Times Good University Guide*'s annual book edition, published by Harper Collins, also includes subject-by-subject analysis,

Oxbridge information and advice on applications, student funding and university life in general.

Rates of graduate employment have always been among our league table's metrics, although the way these are measured has evolved during the *Guide*'s history. In 1999, the career progress of new graduates was tracked using the Destinations of Leavers from Higher Education survey by HESA, which looked at the proportion of graduates who were unemployed six months after finishing their degrees.

Using this yardstick, the ten most successful universities for graduate employment prospects in 1999 were (in order): King's College London, Surrey, UMIST (now part of the University of Manchester), Cranfield, Robert Gordon (Aberdeen), Manchester, Hull, St Andrews and the London School of Economics (LSE), with graduate unemployment six months after graduation ranging from just 1.0 per cent at King's College to 2.6 per cent at LSE.

Conversely, the worst ten universities for job prospects in 1999 were East London, Lincolnshire

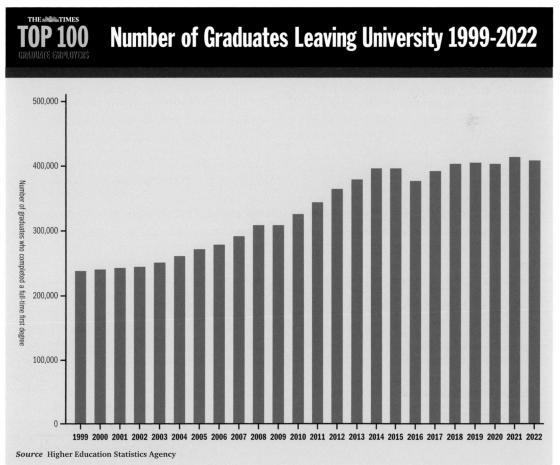

THE TIMES TOP 100 GRADUATE EMPLOYERS — Number of Graduates Leaving University 1999-2022

Source Higher Education Statistics Agency

and Humberside, Paisley, South Bank, Central England (Birmingham), Reading, Thames Valley, Coventry, Teesside and Lampeter. Graduate unemployment six months after leaving these universities ranged from 14.6 per cent at East London to 8.2 per cent for Lampeter.

Interestingly, half of these universities have since undergone rebranding and structural overhauls – such as Thames Valley becoming the University of West London, instituting a raft of changes and improvements, and climbing successfully from the foot of our main league table in 2001 to 40th place in our most recent edition and the top-ranked modern university. Lincolnshire and Humberside, which finished last in 1999's main academic league table, as well as near-bottom for graduate prospects, is now flourishing as the University of Lincoln, holding a gold rating in the government's Teaching Excellence Framework and with much improved graduate prospects.

After several years in the making, a new way of assessing graduate prospects made its debut in 2021. The Graduate Outcomes (GO) survey moved the census point from six months after degrees to 15 months on, to better reflect the changes in work patterns. *The Times & Sunday Times Good University Guide* evolved its measure to accommodate the GO, so we now look at the proportion of graduates in high-skilled jobs or postgraduate study.

The top ten universities for graduate prospects in 2023 are Imperial College London (with 95.2 per cent of graduates achieving the desired outcomes of high-skilled jobs or further study 15 months after their degrees), followed by Cambridge, St George's London, Oxford, Bath, the London School of Economics, Durham, St Andrews, University College London and Warwick.

Bringing up the rear for graduate prospects this year are the University of the Creative Arts (with just 52.2 per cent of graduates in high-skilled jobs or further study 15 months on), Arts University Bournemouth (57.4 per cent), University of the Arts London (59.3 per cent), London Metropolitan (60.2 per cent), Falmouth (60.6 per cent), Bath Spa (61.9 per cent), Leeds Arts (62.4 per cent), Roehampton (62.4 per cent), University of Wales Trinity St David (62.6 per cent) and Southampton Solent (63.3 per cent). The preponderance of arts-focused institutions at the bottom of the pile for graduate prospects is unlikely to be a surprise for those considering creative courses, who in most cases understand that progression in arts careers

can often fall outside the 15 months timescale.

These latest GO figures reveal the stark difference between institutions on rates of graduate employment but recent research from the Institute of Fiscal Studies shows that 80 per cent of graduates do end up better off financially from higher education, with a typical male graduate making about £130,000 more over his lifetime, while female graduates earn around £100,000 more than those without a degree.

But one in five graduates will earn less during their working life than if they had not gone to university, the same IFS report shows, while the top 10 per cent of graduates can expect an average gain of at least £500,0000 over their lifetime, compared with those without a degree.

Today's students are all too aware of the cost of a university education. Following the £1,000 up-front fees introduced in 1998, student maintenance grants were turned into loans the year after. So-called 'variable tuition fees' were introduced in 2006, available through a loan rather than up-front, and although universities were able to set their own fees, almost all charged the maximum rate of £3,000 per year. Six years later these trebled to £9,000, sparking protests and student riots, and edged up by £250 in 2017 to make £9,250 – where they have remained since.

According to *The UK Graduate Careers Survey 2023* produced by High Fliers Research, the average student debt for new graduates from the 'Class of 2023' was an eye-watering £43,000. And students starting a degree in 2023 will also have to get their heads around the extended loan repayment terms of forty years and a lower repayment threshold of £27,295 when they start work.

Data compiled for our *Guide* reveals that the highest-earning graduates command salaries nearly double those of the lowest paid, and employment rates vary wildly between subjects. Medicine, nursing, dentistry, radiography, veterinary medicine and physiotherapy offer some of the best rates of employment – ranging from 89 per cent to 95 per cent in high-skilled jobs 15 months after graduation.

For graduate starting salaries, economics and engineering degrees promise a premium, while dentistry tops the scale at £39,000 according to the latest figures, followed by medicine (£34,000), veterinary science (£31,000), natural sciences (£30,000). Social work, perhaps surprisingly, is also among the ten highest-earning subjects

Expect more ___

Go further with Freshfields

Embark on an extraordinary legal career. At Freshfields, you will help the world's leading international organisations solve their most complex legal challenges.

From high-profile, precedent-setting work that transcends borders to complex cross-border matters, we empower you to transform challenges into opportunities.

Join Freshfields and expect more than you ever imagined.

£50k starting, rising to £125k on qualifying

100 trainee places

Unique eight-seat programme

International secondment and pro bono opportunities

Prestigious clients in 150+ countries

Learn more: **freshfields.com/ukgraduates**

 Freshfields

for graduate salaries – with median earnings for recent graduates of £28,000.

At the opposite end of the scale, the lowest employment rates are among criminology graduates (34 per cent in high-skilled jobs 15 months after degrees), animal science (35 per cent), hospitality, leisure, recreation and tourism (44 per cent) and drama, dance and cinematics (45 per cent).

Also impacting the graduate employment landscape is the steep upturn in the number of graduates being awarded Firsts and 2.1 degrees – particularly over the past 15 years, as university tuition fees and student debts have risen. In 1999, 51 per cent of graduates earned a first or 2.1 but this proportion had risen annually since and reached 79 per cent in 2022. Consequently, most major employers have implemented their own testing and assessments to sift through applicants, rather than relying on graduates' degree classifications during the recruitment process.

Throughout these 25 years of change, the overall high quality of UK universities has been unwavering, with British institutions second only to American universities in global league tables.

But amid the diversification of British higher education, the dominance of Oxbridge and the Russell Group has been diluted. These universities remain highly-rated and perennially occupy the upper reaches of *The Times & Sunday Times Good University Guide* – in the 2023 edition, Oxford has returned to the head of the list, St Andrews is in 2nd place, followed by Cambridge.

But many newer institutions are equally popular with students and employers – half the UK graduates recruited in 2022 by employers featured in *The Times Top 100 Graduate Employers* were from a non-Russell Group university. Within the latest *Guide*, Falmouth has jumped an impressive forty-five places to be ranked in 42nd place, one ahead of Nottingham Trent which itself is up thirty-seven places year-on-year.

Wherever you are studying, make university work for you, capitalise on the huge choice of employment that lies beyond your degree, and good luck in your first graduate job.

THE TIMES TOP 100 GRADUATE EMPLOYERS
The Times & Sunday Times Good University Guide 2023

	2022			2022	
1	2	UNIVERSITY OF OXFORD	26	18	KING'S COLLEGE LONDON
2	1	UNIVERSITY OF ST ANDREWS	27	27	UNIVERSITY OF EAST ANGLIA
3	3	UNIVERSITY OF CAMBRIDGE	28	24	QUEEN'S UNIVERSITY BELFAST
4	5	LONDON SCHOOL OF ECONOMICS	29	26	ROYAL HOLLOWAY, UNIVERSITY OF LONDON
5	4	IMPERIAL COLLEGE LONDON	30	28	UNIVERSITY OF NOTTINGHAM
6	6	DURHAM UNIVERSITY	31	34	UNIVERSITY OF READING
7	7	UNIVERSITY COLLEGE LONDON	32	36	UNIVERSITY OF DUNDEE
8	9	UNIVERSITY OF BATH	33	30	UNIVERSITY OF LIVERPOOL
9	8	UNIVERSITY OF WARWICK	34	42	NEWCASTLE UNIVERSITY
10	13	UNIVERSITY OF EDINBURGH	35	37	UNIVERSITY OF LEICESTER
11	10	LOUGHBOROUGH UNIVERSITY	36	40	QUEEN MARY, UNIVERSITY OF LONDON
12	11	LANCASTER UNIVERSITY	37	33	SOAS, UNIVERSITY OF LONDON
13	21	UNIVERSITY OF EXETER	38	41	UNIVERSITY OF STIRLING
14	12	UNIVERSITY OF GLASGOW	39	44	ULSTER UNIVERSITY
15	14	UNIVERSITY OF BRISTOL	40	74	UNIVERSITY OF WEST LONDON
16	16	UNIVERSITY OF SOUTHAMPTON	41	38	ABERYSTWYTH UNIVERSITY
17	19	UNIVERSITY OF YORK	42	87	FALMOUTH UNIVERSITY
18	17	UNIVERSITY OF STRATHCLYDE, GLASGOW	43	70	NOTTINGHAM TRENT UNIVERSITY
19	20	UNIVERSITY OF ABERDEEN	44	39	SWANSEA UNIVERSITY
20	25	UNIVERSITY OF BIRMINGHAM	45	45	ASTON UNIVERSITY
21	22	UNIVERSITY OF SHEFFIELD	46	64	BANGOR UNIVERSITY
22	32	UNIVERSITY OF SURREY	47	29	HARPER ADAMS UNIVERSITY
23	15	UNIVERSITY OF LEEDS	48	46	UNIVERSITY OF KENT
24	23	UNIVERSITY OF MANCHESTER	49	62	NORTHUMBRIA UNIVERSITY
25	35	CARDIFF UNIVERSITY	50	47	UNIVERSITY OF SUSSEX

Source The Times & Sunday Times Good University Guide

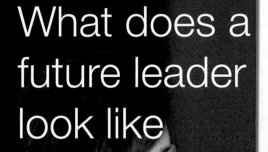

What does a
future leader
look like

today?

We're building a bank that's fit for
the future, now. It's why we welcome
applications to our Global Internships
and Graduate Programmes from
students and graduates with any
degree, from any background.

hsbc.com/earlycareers

 HSBC

Start in the classroom.

Where you go from there is up to you.

Teaching translates your passion for your subject into a career that's **life-changing** – not just for you, but for those you teach.

It's incredibly rewarding – in more ways than one. After your year of teacher training, you'll start on a salary of **£28k-£34k**; depending on where you teach. You'll also receive a generous holiday allowance of up to 13 weeks.

Progression in teaching is quick, with roles available both inside and outside the classroom as you become more experienced. Those who move on to the Senior Leadership Team in their school could earn a salary anywhere between **£50,122** and **£123,057, or up to £131,353 in inner London.**

Most importantly, you'll get the chance to shape lives every day, witnessing first-hand the impact your career can have on the next generation.

It starts here.

Search: **Get Into Teaching**

Department
for Education

Amy Rob
Primary Scho

"There are endless positives of training to be a teacher. Although theory-based learning is so valuable, the true highlight is being on placement – in the classroom – experiencing what life as a teacher really is like. It is just wonderful.

The best feeling is knowing that each day is a step closer to the end goal. My first year of teaching has been one I will never forget. I've loved building a classroom full of inspired individuals, eager to learn.

Sharing knowledge together has been empowering; knowing that 30 little learners are looking up to you is a truly magical feeling.

Lightbulb moments; small, big, even tiny achievements that each child has made leaves me bursting with pride."

Teaching ☑

Every Lesson Shapes a Life

Front|ine

Making social work better for children

Alex joined the Frontline programme in 2022. He currently works in an assessment and intervention team and now earns £31,000.

This is the work where you'll build the skills to help keep children safe from harm

Join our **Frontline programme** and become a children's social worker. You'll help keep children safe from harm and create positive change for them and their families.

You'll get three years of paid training and support while working in a local council social work team.

Qualify as a social worker, complete a fully-funded master's degree and learn how to work with families to protect vulnerable children.

We won't lie; it's a challenging profession. You'll help families living in the toughest circumstances and struggling with a range of pressures.

But it's also one of the most rewarding careers. The programme is designed to give you the support you'll need to thrive in the role, and the work you do will change lives for the better.

This is the work that makes a difference. This is social work.

Qualify as a social worker and complete a master's degree

Earn while you train with a tax excempt bursary in year one, and a £27,000+ salary from year two

Receive ongoing support with your career through the Fellowship

Graduate Lives

Interviews by **Martin Birchall**

THE TIMES
TOP 100
GRADUATE EMPLOYERS

Telling the stories of graduates from the past 25 years working at Britain's top graduate employers.

Your future

Realise your **potential** at Enterprise

Join us on our award-winning Management Trainee programme or as an Intern and you'll enjoy great benefits, excellent training and real responsibility from day one. It starts in one of our 10,000 branches worldwide. It continues with you becoming a leader of one of those branches, in as little as two years' time. From there, you can go in whatever direction you choose. Marketing? Finance? Human resources? The choice is yours.

Get started now
careers.enterprise.co.uk

CLASS OF 1999

Auditing a lifetime of success

Just as the launch edition of *The Times Top 100 Graduate Employers* was published in 1999, new graduate Kelly Dunn was preparing to start work with the firm at number eight in the inaugural employer rankings.

Kelly Dunn, Audit Partner, KPMG

Dunn had studied for an accounting and management information systems degree at the University of Hertfordshire.

"I'd applied to universities like Warwick and Lancaster too, but I preferred the smaller, more intimate environment at Hertfordshire's business school," she remembers.

By her final year at university, having completed a summer internship at a large corporate bank, Dunn had decided she wanted to join one of the large accountancy firms.

"I applied to Arthur Andersen, KPMG and PwC – three of what was then the 'Big Five' accounting firms," she says. "I knew KPMG quite well because they'd sponsored awards at my university and when it came to the interviews, I really enjoyed the people I interacted with at the firm."

She accepted their job offer and started work as a trainee auditor at the St Albans office. "I chose audit because of the variety it offered. I wanted to work with a myriad of different clients and get the broadest experience I could," Dunn explains.

"As an auditor, I could go into any business, in any sector, in any location, at any stage of its business life cycle – and that was its appeal." She travelled the country auditing end-of-year accounts and financial reports for the firm's clients.

Although she had already studied accountancy for her degree, Dunn found the professional exams that all auditors need to complete very tough. "I actually failed my first exam," she recalls. "I'd left university with a First and hadn't really experienced failure before. But the firm was so supportive, I retook the exam and went on to qualify as a chartered accountant three years later."

Over the next five years, Dunn studied for an executive MBA in Edinburgh and Leuven in Belgium, and progressed from assistant manager to manager.

She set her sights on becoming a senior manager in her local office. "I was ambitious and wanted to run the department, I wanted to know about recruitment and how the finances worked," Dunn explains. "It was

such great experience and helped me understand the way the business operated."

Not long after becoming senior manager, Dunn was seconded to KPMG's London office, to work as executive assistant to one of the firm's youngest partners.

"He was hugely energetic and exciting – and it meant I was suddenly in meetings with the heads of audit and the chairman of the firm," she recounts. "It was a complete change for me because I was doing sales pitches for financial services clients and business development, rather than delivering audits."

Dunn's time in London led to another promotion, this time to become audit director in the firm's Watford office. "I also took on the role of people partner for national markets audit, responsible for pay, recruitment and talent management. It was really enjoyable and I liked the variety it gave me."

Then in November 2015, sixteen years after joining the firm, Dunn was appointed a partner of the firm – thereby becoming a part-owner of the business. "I had been put forward for it by my head of audit and although I wasn't sure I'd be successful, I went into the selection process determined to get the most out of the experience."

Dunn moved to the Cambridge office, as one of three partners, and is now the office's senior partner. "I still spend 70% of my time on audits but the remainder is working on growing the business, leading on operational matters and developing my people for the future, as well as being part of the executive team for the region.

"Much of my focus now is on the next generation who are going to take over this partnership", Dunn continues. "I love supporting new graduates and apprentices who are a couple of years into their careers – as well as the manager and director group – to help shape them and really push their boundaries to be as successful as they can be."

Taking the fast lane to the heart of Government

The Civil Service was named the UK's number one graduate employer in the fifth annual edition of *The Times Top 100 Graduate Employers* in 2003, the same year that new graduate Damian Paterson joined its prestigious Fast Stream programme.

I was always into politics but my school didn't offer it as an A-level," Paterson recalls. "I remember the very early days of Radio Five Live starting. I would be forever listening to it and I found myself really interested in current affairs and international issues. I had an opinion on everything."

He chose to study politics at Loughborough University. "I knew I was going to enjoy the course, but I didn't think when I started that it would lead me into a career in politics," says Paterson. "But so much incredible stuff went on – 9/11 happened while I was at university and I studied in the Czech Republic for a bit, so I saw the transition of post-Cold War countries beginning to join NATO and prepare for EU accession. It fascinated me."

Damian Paterson, former Civil Service Fast Stream participant, now Director of Strategy, People and Culture at the Government Legal Service

At the end of his three-year undergraduate degree, Paterson opted to stay on to do a Masters. "I'd finished top of my year, so Loughborough very kindly gave me an academic scholarship," he remembers. "And I was also playing hockey for the university, so I was really glad to have the extra year for that too."

Paterson had applied for the Civil Service Fast Stream the previous year but hadn't been successful, so re-applied during his Masters.

"The Fast Stream seemed to bring together all the things I wanted to do," he explains. "I was interested in government, but I didn't want to be a politician. And I was interested in international affairs, so it was a great combination of things that took me there."

He was offered a place on the Fast Stream, just as the Iraq War was beginning, and started work at the Ministry of Defence in autumn 2003.

"I'd originally hoped to become a diplomat, but the Foreign Office was one of the most over-subscribed parts of the Fast Stream," admits Paterson. "But I was really excited to be joining the MoD because I'd briefly considered a career in the Army and both my parents worked in the RAF."

"I remember getting my first-ever brown envelope with 'On Her Majesty's Service' on it, with my first assignment and where I was going to work," he continues. "I read the first couple of lines and it said 'you will be working on the Ministry of Defence's response to the Hutton Report'."

At the time, the inquiry chaired by Lord Hutton was in full flow, investigating the death of Dr David Kelly, an MoD employee and former UN weapons inspector in Iraq – and examining whether the Government had exaggerated Iraq's military capabilities and weapons of mass destruction, in the build-up to the Iraq war.

"To be working on this, which was a major scandal at the time and had such huge media attention, was just amazing," says Paterson. "I remember on my second day in the department, I had to go the Permanent Secretary's office and was listening to a conversation about some of the work that I would be involved in. I realised then that I'd just stepped into this world of high politics."

When the Hutton Report was published a few months later, Paterson's work was included in a speech by Prime Minister Tony Blair. "It was probably only about three or four sentences. But I'd written them. And it's always stuck with me to this day, that sense of privilege and pride, when a minister stands up in parliament and says something that you've written – or you've helped shape a policy or issue. That's been one of my overriding motivations for the last twenty years in this job."

Paterson's time on the Hutton Report was just the first of five Fast Stream placements in different parts of the MoD. "When I got promoted at the end of the Fast Stream, I went and worked for Sir John Chilcot, on the first two-and-a-bit years of his inquiry into the Iraq war", he recounts. "It was absolutely extraordinary, probably the best job I will do in my lifetime, in terms of content and learning about how the government is such a complex place."

He continues: "One of things I've enjoyed most in this career – and what has continued to motivate me – is you genuinely get to work on things that are on the front of the newspapers, and you actually know what's going on with them."

For Paterson, the Fast Stream was the foundation of a seventeen-year career within the MoD.

"I spent time in the defence press office with John Reid as Secretary of State when Afghanistan was starting to ramp up," he says. "I've helped buy nuclear submarines and strategic weapons systems, and I've looked after civil service colleagues in Iraq and Afghanistan. And at one point I was commuting to Washington and back and had a portfolio that took me from Singapore to the Falkland Islands."

Paterson's final five years at the MoD was at the Army's headquarters in Salisbury, working as the link between the department, ministers and government and the Army.

He moved to the Cabinet Office in 2019 before taking up his current post as Director of Strategy, People and Culture at the Government Legal Department two years ago.

"We've got legal teams in almost every Whitehall department who help shape the law, producing the law in terms of secondary legislation – and when we have to, we defend the government's policies and course of action in the courts," he explains.

"I'm responsible for setting the department's strategy and making sure we have the capability to deliver it. I look at how we meet ministers' expectations and the public's needs, but also how do we create a people environment where we have enough lawyers and other professionals with the right skills in the department."

Twenty years into his career, Paterson is now just two levels below permanent secretary, the Civil Service's title for the head of a government department.

"Would I like to be more senior and make a positive impact on an even bigger scope of society, a bigger scope of how government works? Absolutely," he muses.

"But what I'm increasingly learning is that the ultimate is to feel you're doing a really great job and that you're making a difference, and that you're helping to nurture the incredibly important institution that the Civil Service is, to make sure governments in ten, twenty and thirty years' time have the benefit of a really capable Civil Service."

How The Times reported the Civil Service reaching number one in the new Top 100 rankings in October 2003

Rhiannon Rumfitt, Senior Test Engineer, Airbus

CLASS OF 2008

Engineering a high-flying career

Rhiannon Rumfitt's love of maths and science launched her engineering career at aircraft manufacturer Airbus.

There is very much a right or wrong with engineering – there's plenty of creativity but there's always maths and science behind it and that's what I really enjoy about engineering," says Rumfitt.

She studied for a Master's in integrated engineering at Cardiff University, combining mechanical and electrical engineering.

"While I was at university I had two really successful summer placements at Airbus UK's Filton site in Bristol," remembers Rumfitt. "They gave me a great insight to the business and got me hooked. I worked with people on the graduate scheme and I knew then it was what I wanted to do."

She also had a strong connection to the site. "My Dad worked there and ever since I was small, he brought me to the 'bring your daughter to work' days and my Mum and Aunty worked on site for a while too," she explains. "And my brother did an internship there as well, so Filton means a lot to my family."

Rumfitt applied to Airbus UK in her final year at university and was offered a place on its graduate scheme, starting in September 2008

as a structures engineer. Over the next two years, she completed a series of three-month placements in different engineering disciplines at Filton, as well as a manufacturing placement at the Airbus site at Broughton in the north-east of Wales.

"Switching between placements wasn't easy but the graduate scheme gave me great skills in terms of how to present yourself and the confidence to move around from team to team," Rumfitt recalls.

"And I was also fortunate to do an 'out of business' placement at an airline in New Zealand. It was a really good opportunity to see how the customer uses our products and the problems they face, so you can understand the relationship between the customer and Airbus – and take that experience back to the business."

By the end of the graduate scheme, Rumfitt knew that the area of engineering she was most interested in was stress analysis. She went on to work as a stress engineer within the product engineering division at Airbus, working on a series of different aircraft programmes at Filton, before going on secondment

to Airbus' engineering centre at Wichita, Kansas in the US.

"We were doing stress analysis of one of our products and I went out there with a view to learning how they analyse that particular component and then bring it back to the UK," explains Rumfitt. This experience helped her go on to become a lead engineer, managing internal teams and external suppliers, working on the development of new products.

"As an engineer within Airbus, you can go into technical leadership or programme leadership which is what I've done," she reflects. "I think my technical background, integrating both mechanical and electrical engineering, has been fundamental to that and has really helped me."

After eleven years at the company and two periods of maternity leave, Rumfitt decided it was time for a change. "I'm now based in the Airbus UK Structures Test Centre and I love it, it's just fantastic," she enthuses. The centre conducts digital and physical testing on the components that are used on Airbus aircraft.

"This could be small pieces of material where we're trying to find out its mechanical properties, right up to big component tests like a full-scale wing which we're testing to see how it will work when it's in service," explains Rumfitt. "A test specimen arrives, you can physically see it, it's tangible – and then it goes into the test facility and you can see it being tested. That gives me a lot of energy."

Rumfitt has now been an engineer at Airbus for fifteen years but still gets excited at the airport when she sees aircraft that she has worked on.

"There's a unique feature of one particular aircraft that really dictated two and a half years of my early career. I was working on its design, development and what it was going to look like. To see it now, physically on the aircraft is a great satisfaction," she smiles. "It's really obvious when you're onboard, so I do take a lot of pride pointing it out, especially to my children."

Imagine
What's Next

Find a bright future as a Lloyds Banking Group graduate

The world is constantly evolving. New knowledge and technologies are impacting how people bank every day. To meet the ever-changing needs of our customers, we're looking for graduates with a wide range of skills and interests to explore the possibilities of this transformation.

SOLVE PROBLEMS.
SAVE LIVES.

Software Developer: **£60k**

Business Analyst: **£60k**

Technical Engineer: **£60k**

Service Analyst: **£35k**

Account Manager: **£60k**

Implementation Specialist: **£35k**

NO EXPERIENCE REQUIRED

www.tpp-careers.com

f TPP Careers   🐦 @TPPCareers

📷 @tpp_careers   in TPP

Learning to tackle educational disadvantage

In the year that *The Times Top 100 Graduate Employers* reached its fifteenth edition, the Teach First programme celebrated its tenth anniversary. Jon Hutchinson was one of more than 1,500 graduates who joined the scheme that summer.

Hutchinson was studying for a philosophy degree at Heythrop College, then a specialist philosophy and theology college that was part of the University of London, when he applied for the Teach First programme.

"I was a classic philosophy student and had no idea what I wanted to do after university. But I started to get a bit panicky in my final year, so in October I went online to *The Times Top 100 Graduate Employers* website and thought I'd literally apply for the whole of the top ten," he laughs.

"I'd not heard of Teach First before, but they were at number three and although teaching didn't appeal to me, I liked their moral mission and the fact that it wouldn't be an office job," he continues. "And I found the exclusivity of it attractive – they made it very clear that they rejected three out of four candidates who applied."

Hutchinson's application was successful and by Christmas he'd been offered a place on Teach First's 2013 intake. The first part of the programme is its 'summer institute', a six-week intensive training course for all its new joiners. "My summer institute was in Warwick and was loads of fun," Hutchinson remembers. "It brought together this incredible set of like-minded people fresh out of university, to prepare them before they were placed in schools".

Because Hutchinson's degree wasn't in a specialist subject taught in secondary schools, like maths or history, he was asked to become a primary school teacher. He began by teaching Year 3 children at a school in Enfield Lock in north London.

"On my first day, I'd got my classroom ready and I remember thinking the children are going to come in and I'll be in charge of them,"

Jon Hutchinson, former Teach First participant, now Director of Training & Development at the Reach Foundation

he says. "I kept imagining someone was going to walk in the door and say 'you didn't think we were going to let you do that, did you'? The last time I'd met an eight year-old was when I was one myself."

Hutchinson found the first few weeks a very steep learning curve. "It was extraordinarily tough and exhausting. And it was a humbling experience too because you're told throughout the summer institute that you're going to help eradicate educational disadvantage," he explains. "And then you turn up at your school and you're just a bit of a crap teacher. It made doing a bad lesson feel ten times worse."

And it wasn't just the classroom teaching that Hutchinson found challenging. "There weren't really any holidays because I was studying for my PGCE as well," he says. "You'd get to half term and instead of using the time to rest and recover, it was time to write an essay."

With his PGCE done, Hutchinson

went on to teach Year 6 pupils in his second year. "The support from Teach First during my time on the programme was genuinely excellent. They made regular visits to the school and were on-tap with whatever help you needed."

At the end of the two years, Teach First participants can elect to remain within teaching or education, or move into a different career area. "For me, there was no question, I was definitely staying in teaching and in the classroom," says Hutchinson.

But he opted to move to a different school for his third year in teaching. "I'd heard Ed Vainker, one of the Teach First ambassadors from the first year of the programme in 2003, talking about how he had set up a free school with Rebecca Cramer, another Teach First ambassador, and I knew I wanted to go and work there."

Hutchinson joined the Reach Academy Felton in autumn 2015 as head of Year 2. "As well as being a brand-new school, it was unusual because it took children from aged two all the way to 18-year-olds and had been set up to be really small – just sixty pupils per year group," he explains. "For me, it was a huge privilege to be part of it. A couple of years before I joined, Ofsted rated the school as 'outstanding', and it went on to get some of the best GCSE results in the country," he continues. "Its success gave it a national profile, with prime ministers and the Royal Family visiting the school."

Over the next three years, Hutchinson went from being head of Year 2 to head of Year 4 but was increasingly spending more time developing the school's curriculum. "We'd felt that the content in a lot of the foundation subjects, like history and geography, was very light in many primary schools," he explains. "The caricature was that primary schools spent all morning doing really rigorous, systematic maths and English lessons. And then in the afternoon they'd have a history lesson and make Stonehenge out of biscuits."

Hutchinson's school bid for a new curriculum fund that the Government had established, as part of its drive to improve the curriculum. "I'd started writing about the curriculum and speaking at conferences," he explains. "It caught the attention of the schools minister Nick Gibb, so I worked on various Department for Education (DfE) groups and our school won the funding bid. It meant I spent a year writing curriculum resources and supporting twelve other schools around the country who were implementing it."

The idea was to provide succinct, content-rich work booklets that teachers could use to ensure every child developed a substantive knowledge of each topic.

"The lightbulb moment for me was when I'd been teaching Year 3 during my time with Teach First and I was told to do pre-historic Britain in history. And I said, 'OK, so what do I teach them?' and the answer came

back that you had to decide what to cover," he remembers.

"It seemed crazy to me. We've been teaching children about the Stone Age for about fifty years and yet, here am I with zero years' experience trying to write this from scratch. I knew it wasn't going to be any good and so it become an ethical thing for me – you can't guarantee an excellent teacher in front of every child but at least you could guarantee a great curriculum for them, because you can write that down."

The resources developed by Hutchinson and the Reach Academy Felton proved to be highly successful and went on to be used by more than 175 schools nationwide. They have recently been acquired by Pearson, the education publisher.

After working on curriculum development, Hutchinson returned to teaching and became assistant head of the primary school but continued to be involved with several external projects. "I was on the DfE's teacher recruitment and retention working group and helped write what is now the early careers framework, which sets out the training and knowledge that new teachers need to have before they qualify," he says. "It was really interesting work that felt like it would have a big impact."

Hutchinson also worked as a tutor for a new teacher training course. "The Ambition Institute were offering a Master's in expert teaching and I was seconded to do one day a week as a tutor on the course," he enthuses.

And at the beginning of the pandemic, Hutchinson was part of the team that launched and ran the Oak National Academy, providing online lessons that schools across the country could use during the lockdowns.

"We were filming daily lessons for use by students in all year groups and for every subject – I led the humanities subjects for primary schools. I recorded about a hundred lessons myself and overall we filmed around 650 lessons for use by

schools around the country. It was an incredible project."

After six years at Reach Academy Feltham, Hutchinson took the difficult decision to step away from teaching and is now director of training & development for the recently-established Reach Foundation.

"At Reach, we developed what we call a 'cradle to career' approach, where we offer better pre-school support for parents in the community before kids start school, as well as better ongoing support after they've left secondary school," he explains.

"We think of schools as being anchor institutions that are hubs of communities and coordinate broader services. My job with the Foundation is to work with about thirty trusts around the country who are keen to develop similar models for their own schools. I support them to develop an 'all-through curriculum' across their primaries and secondaries, as well as thinking about their broader community."

He's also been appointed as an international fellow for the Learning Sciences Exchange, a US think-tank. "It brings together representatives from North and South America, Europe and Africa from the different disciplines of educational leadership, research, entertainment, journalism and entrepreneurship and we're looking at how to leverage the learning sciences to support children and families. It's fascinating to get such a global, multi-disciplinary perspective on things."

Hutchinson is proud to be an ambassador for Teach First and has just taken part in its twentieth anniversary celebrations.

"There are so few organisations that focus on educational disadvantage in the way that Teach First does and it has created this amazing movement of motivated and passionate people to tackle it head-on. There is a sense of belonging and a shared purpose that is so galvanising and is seared into your identity – I've felt it throughout the ten years since I joined."

We are hiring Graduates and Interns

SCAN ME FOR
CORPORATE ROLES

SCAN ME FOR
OPERATIONS ROLES

Come build the future with us

Aiming high in the legal world

Michelle Blake made the most of work experience to take her from university in Dublin to become a solicitor at a top London law firm.

MATEJ KING

Michelle Blake, Tax Assoxiate, Slaughter and May

I grew up in Ireland and although I knew when I was at school that law would be a good career option, I was also very interested in the business side of things as well, says Blake. "So, I decided for my university degree I would take a split approach and study both."

She chose the four-year business and law programme at University College Dublin and used the university holidays to build up useful work experience.

"In my first summer I went over to New York and did an internship in a small law firm there, which was amazing and a great introduction to the way things are done in the US," Blake explains. "Then in my second year I did another summer internship, this time at an international telecommunications company, where I worked in their legal and regulatory department."

In her third year at university, Blake applied for a place on the summer scheme at Slaughter and May in London. "I knew a lot about the big Dublin law firms, but not so

much about those in the UK," she remembers. "My academic adviser at university had worked at Slaughter and May and she recommended that I apply."

Blake's application was successful and she spent three weeks with the firm. "It was a fantastic time, with talks on all the different practice areas and the type of work it does, and the chance to speak to people at every level, from trainees to partners," she recalls. "It left me with a very positive impression of the firm."

At the end of her internship, Blake was interviewed and was offered a training contract with the firm. She graduated the following year, in the summer of 2018, but needed to study additional modules on UK law before she could begin the Legal Practice Course (LPC) in London.

"At the time, the LPC was an intensive training course that all solicitors completed before they began a training contract with a firm," she explains. The LPC has since been replaced by the Solicitors Qualifying Examination (SQE).

Blake joined Slaughter and May in March 2020. Her two-year training contract included a series of three-month and six-month rotations within the firm, known as 'seats'.

"The pandemic meant it was a very strange time to be starting a training contract," she reflects. "But I was still able to do seats in four different departments – corporate, competition, disputes and investigations, and tax – as well as a client secondment with Burberry."

Each seat is designed to give trainees first-hand experience of the work the firm does, as well as help them choose which type of legal work they want to specialise in once they qualify as a solicitor.

"I'd had quite a bit of tax experience while I was in Ireland, so knew it was the area I was most interested in," says Blake. She qualified as a solicitor in early 2022 and is now working as an associate in the tax department.

"We do a lot of work on corporate transactions, disputes with tax authorities, and general advisory and consultancy work for our clients, who are usually large FTSE 100 or FTSE 250 companies," she explains. "They come to us for advice on a wide range of matters, for example the tax implications of entering into an agreement to acquire another company, or re-structuring a group of companies."

Blake acknowledges that being a solicitor at a top corporate law firm can involve working long hours. "You can't expect it to be a nine to five job because we are a client-facing industry, which means there are times when you do work late into the night, in order to complete a transaction and meet the deadline. But there is still a good work-life balance, with times that are less busy too."

"I'm loving London, it's one of my favourite cities and such an exciting place to live," she enthuses. "I definitely see myself staying with Slaughter and May for the foreseeable future."

Sam McPherson, Commercial Management Trainee, L'Oréal

CLASS OF 2023

All set for the beauty business

Sam McPherson left university in the summer of 2023 and has just started work at a graduate employer that has been ranked in all twenty-five annual editions of *The Times Top 100 Graduate Employers*.

I'm so excited to have been accepted onto the commercial graduate scheme at L'Oréal," says McPherson. "It's an amazing opportunity and means I'll be doing three rotational placements over the next 18 months, in different parts of the business, like marketing and account management."

For McPherson, it's the culmination of a journey that began four years earlier. "When I was at school, I didn't really have any idea what I'd want to do for a career," he remembers. "I was doing history, theatre studies and photography for my A-levels but rather than study any of those at university, I chose to apply for business courses. I thought it'd be a great opportunity to learn about different business functions and develop lots of useful knowledge."

After making his UCAS application, McPherson's first choice was business & management with marketing at the University of Exeter. "But my A-level results weren't what I'd hoped for and I missed the grades I needed," he recounts. "I was so upset but Exeter offered me an alternative place on the business course at their Penryn campus near Falmouth in Cornwall."

It was a big change for McPherson but he accepted the offer and started his four-year degree in September 2019. "I wasn't a very maths person and one of the first modules we did was on finance and I thought, I've made a mistake here, I should have stuck with history," he says. "But after that first two-week wobble, I knew I'd definitely made the right choice. I loved the course, I loved the area and Falmouth was brilliant."

The start of the pandemic in March 2020 brought McPherson's first year to an abrupt halt. "I was at the beach swimming with my friends when we had a text from the university and then an email to say the campus would be shutting," he remembers. "I went home the next day and we did everything online for the rest of the year, including our summer exams."

McPherson returned to Falmouth in July but lectures and coursework remained fully-online throughout his second year at university too. The third year of his degree was a placement and after applying to a number of well-known employers, he landed a place at L'Oréal, based in its Hammersmith headquarters.

"It was a 12-month placement in the commercial function, the part of the business that manages the relationship between the company and the buyers of our products, like high street and online retailers," McPherson explains. "It was an absolutely brilliant experience, I was supporting national account managers and was being given more and more responsibility as the year went on."

His placement was due to finish in July 2022 but McPherson was asked to stay on. "The opportunity came up for me to do an extra three months and I was actually given my own account to manage," he recalls. "I was negotiating the commercial terms and dealing with the price list myself. I ended up closing the deal in September just before I went back to university and then by December the stores were popping up with our brands in there. It was a very, very proud moment for me to walk down the street and be able to say 'that's my work'."

Internships at L'Oréal do not automatically lead to a place on the company's graduate programme, so McPherson was re-interviewed at the end of his placement. "Because interns are assessed alongside external applicants, it took until Christmas to hear that I'd been successful. But when they rang to say I'd got it, it was a day of celebrations."

Having graduated with a first-class degree, McPherson began his full-time job in the commercial team at L'Oreal in July and is due to complete the graduate programme in early 2025.

Become part of our story

If you're looking for the perfect environment to
learn, develop and progress, we think you'll
love life here. We're a growing firm (one of
the fastest growing in the world, in fact).
And we work at the heart of sectors that
drive global trade and commerce. It
makes this an unrivalled opportunity
to take on exciting, high-profile
work and to grow as rapidly as us.

DO MORE.
GO FURTHER.
WORK TOGETHER.

Get the support you need to do more from day one.
Work with experts in a high-performing team. Take on
complex challenges and deliver solutions that make
a real change. Build your career by working in a variety
of sectors and industries. Together, let's make
a greater impact. Let's start doing.

To find out if a career in consulting is right for you,
search **Newton Graduate Careers or visit
WorkatNewton.com**

NEWTON

Alicia Middleton, Consultant
Joseph Geldman, Consultant
Yuwei Zhang, Consultant

Student life from every angle

A student subscription gives you unlimited digital access to news, features and comment from The Times and Sunday Times. You can also read inspirational stories of businesses started at university and learn about must-read books. We even provide budgeting tools to help you manage your finances.

To see our latest student offers, visit thetimes.co.uk/student or scan the QR code

THE TIMES
TOP 100
GRADUATE EMPLOYERS

	Page		Page		Page
AECOM	66	Deutsche Bank	114	Microsoft	162
Airbus	68	DLA Piper	116	Morgan Stanley	164
Aldi	70	Dyson	118	Mott Macdonald	166
Amazon	72	Enterprise	120	NatWest Group	168
AON	74	EY	122	Newton	170
Arcadis	76	Freshfields	124	NGDP	172
AstraZeneca	78	Frontline	126	NHS	174
BAE Systems	80	Google	128	P&G	176
Bank of America	82	Grant Thornton	130	Penguin	178
Barclays	84	GSK	132	Pfizer	180
BBC	86	Hogan Lovells	134	Police Now	182
BCG	88	HSBC	136	PwC	184
BDO	90	IBM	138	Rolls-Royce	186
BlackRock	92	J.P. Morgan	140	Royal Navy	188
Bloomberg	94	KPMG	142	Santander	190
British Airways	96	Kubrick	144	Savills	192
BT Group	98	L'Oréal	146	Secret Intelligence Service (MI6)	194
Capgemini	100	Latham & Watkins	148		
Channel 4	102	Lidl	150	Sky	196
Citi	104	Linklaters	152	Slaughter and May	198
Civil Service	106	Lloyds Banking Group	154	Teach First	200
Clyde & Co	108	Mars	156	Unlocked	202
CMS	110	Mazars	158	Vodafone	204
Deloitte	112	MI5 - The Security Service	160	White & Case	206

Index

EMPLOYER	RANK	Acc	Con	Eng	Fin	Gen Mgmt	HR	Inv Bank	Law	Log	Mktg	Media	Prop	Purch	R&D	Retail	Sales	Tech	Other	VACANCIES	Insight	Degree Plc	Summer Int	PAGE
AECOM	62		●	●								●						●		350-400		●	●	66
AIRBUS	42			●	●					●	●		●	●				●		150+		●		68
ALDI	9					●										●				100		●		70
AMAZON	12			●	●	●	●			●								●		200			●	72
AON	82		●		●													●		200		●	●	74
ARCADIS	95		●	●																200				76
ASTRAZENECA	25			●	●	●				●	●				●		●	●		100+		●	●	78
BAE SYSTEMS	28	●	●	●	●	●	●			●								●		800		●	●	80
BANK OF AMERICA	75	●			●			●										●		No fixed quota	●	●	●	82
BARCLAYS	10			●	●	●		●			●					●		●		900+	●	●	●	84
BBC	7			●	●	●		●		●	●	●				●		●		200+		●	●	86
BCG	33		●																	No fixed quota	●		●	88
BDO	68	●																		620		●	●	90
BLACKROCK	79				●		●			●							●	●		100+	●	●	●	92
BLOOMBERG	60			●	●												●	●		350	●	●	●	94
BRITISH AIRWAYS	83			●	●	●				●								●		100	●	●	●	96
BT GROUP	67			●		●								●				●		120	●	●	●	98
CAPGEMINI	98		●	●	●		●											●		600+	●	●	●	100
CHANNEL 4	66			●	●	●				●	●						●	●		50		●		102
CITI	89			●				●										●		200+	●	●	●	104
CIVIL SERVICE	2			●	●	●	●						●	●	●			●		1,000			●	106
CLYDE & CO	58								●											75+				108
CMS	65								●											95			●	110
DELOITTE	4	●	●		●				●									●		1,500+	●	●	●	112
DEUTSCHE BANK	70			●			●	●										●		100+	●	●	●	114
DLA PIPER	51								●											50+		●		116
DYSON	50			●	●		●				●			●				●		100		●	●	118
ENTERPRISE	97					●										●	●			1,600		●	●	120
EY	6	●	●		●				●									●		1,000+	●	●	●	122
FRESHFIELDS	44								●											100		●		124
FRONTLINE	63																		●	500			●	126
GOOGLE	5		●	●			●										●	●		No fixed quota			●	128
GRANT THORNTON	90	●	●		●															350-400		●	●	130
GSK	14			●	●		●				●	●		●	●		●			50+		●	●	132
HOGAN LOVELLS	72								●											Up to 50	●		●	134
HSBC	13			●	●		●											●		600+	●	●	●	136

EMPLOYER	RANK	Accountancy	Consulting	Engineering	Finance	General Management	Human Resources	Investment Banking	Law	Logistics	Marketing	Media	Property	Purchasing	Research & Development	Retail	Sales	Technology	Other	VACANCIES	Insight Courses	Degree Placements	Summer Internships	PAGE
IBM	38		●															●		150+				138
J.P. MORGAN	11	●	●		●	●	●	●							●		●	●		500	●	●	●	140
KPMG	8	●	●		●	●			●									●		1,000+		●	●	142
KUBRICK	85		●	●														●		700+				144
L'ORÉAL	19			●						●	●		●							25-35	●		●	146
LATHAM & WATKINS	86								●											32				148
LIDL	26				●					●			●	●						20-30				150
LINKLATERS	23								●											100	●		●	152
LLOYDS BANKING GROUP	20	●		●	●		●	●										●		100+	●	●	●	154
MARS	96			●	●	●					●			●						25				156
MAZARS	94	●	●		●													●		300-350		●	●	158
MI5 - THE SECURITY SERVICE	74			●	●	●												●	●	200+	●	●	●	160
MICROSOFT	30		●						●								●	●		No fixed quota		●		162
MORGAN STANLEY	32	●		●	●		●	●		●			●				●	●		300+	●	●	●	164
MOTT MACDONALD	84		●	●								●						●		500		●	●	166
NATWEST GROUP	36	●			●		●	●										●		350	●	●	●	168
NEWTON	24		●																	185			●	170
NGDP	57					●														250+				172
NHS	3	●			●	●	●											●		250				174
P&G	31			●	●		●				●	●		●			●	●		100		●	●	176
PENGUIN	39	●		●		●				●	●		●	●	●	●			250	●		●	178
PFIZER	49		●	●	●						●	●		●				●		30-50		●	●	180
POLICE NOW	43																		●	400+				182
PWC	1	●	●		●				●									●		1,800+	●	●	●	184
ROLLS-ROYCE	34		●		●													●		No fixed quota		●	●	186
ROYAL NAVY	48		●	●	●	●		●	●		●		●					●		No fixed quota	●	●	●	188
SANTANDER	61		●		●											●				50				190
SAVILLS	76			●								●						●		100+	●	●	●	192
SIS (MI6)	92			●	●	●											●	●	●	100+			●	194
SKY	41	●		●	●	●					●	●					●	●		232			●	196
SLAUGHTER AND MAY	37								●											95	●		●	198
TEACH FIRST	15																	●		1,750	●			200
UNLOCKED	22																	●		143				202
VODAFONE	52			●	●	●					●					●	●		100+				204
WHITE & CASE	64								●											50	●	●	●	206

ALL TOGETHER
MI5

ALL TOGETHER
MI6

GRADUATE
CAREERS
WITH THE UK'S
INTELLIGENCE
SERVICES

***

ALL TOGETHER
GCHQ

SECURITYSERVICE
MI5

**SECRET
INTELLIGENCE
SERVICE** MI6

GCHQ

ALL TOGETHER
STRONGER.

A CAREER WITHIN THE UK INTELLIGENCE SERVICES.

At the UK Intelligence Services, we believe that with the right mix of minds, anything is possible. So, we don't recruit a specific 'type' of person. Instead, we're committed to building a workforce that reflects the society we serve. Why? Because keeping the UK's people, businesses and interests safe requires a real mix of skills, experiences, and backgrounds.

Each service has a slightly different remit, but we're united by one aim: protecting the UK at home and overseas. It's a rewarding job, done by people just like you. From operational and STEM roles to our mission-critical business support functions, your unique insights, talents and perspectives won't just be vital – they'll be valued. All of our people play a key role within the intelligence community. And with a truly diverse workforce, we'll be all together stronger.

MI5 safeguards the UK against threats such as terrorism and espionage. Working alongside our partners, we investigate suspect individuals and organisations, analyse and assess secret intelligence, and find ways to keep the country safe.
Find us at: www.mi5.gov.uk/careers

MI6 protects the security and economic wellbeing of the UK from overseas threats such as international terrorism and the spread of weapons. With our foreign partners, we work secretly around the world and in the UK to stay ahead of our adversaries.
Discover more: www.sis.gov.uk

GCHQ uses cutting-edge technology to unlock the complex world of data and communications. Using the ingenuity of our people, we keep the UK and its citizens safe from cyber-attacks, terrorism and serious crime, both in the real world and online.
Learn more: www.gchq-careers.co.uk

AECOM

AECOM is the world's trusted infrastructure consulting firm, delivering professional services throughout the project lifecycle from planning, design and engineering to programme and construction management, on projects spanning transport, buildings, water, new energy and the environment.

AECOM graduates make a real difference to both the built and natural environment. AECOM services include building engineering, environment, bridges, roads, rail, water, surveying, project management, planning, energy and architecture. Delivering clean water and energy. Building iconic skyscrapers. Planning new cities. Restoring damaged environments. Connecting people and economies with roads, bridges, tunnels and transit systems. Designing parks where children play.

Worldwide, AECOM designs, builds, finances, operates, and manages projects and programmes that unlock opportunities, protect the environment, and improve people's lives.

The AECOM Graduate Development Programme lasts for two years, and will provide graduates with full financial and development support towards their relevant professional qualification, including mentoring, residential training modules, an opportunity to work on live client projects, external training courses where required, and multi-disciplinary exposure.

AECOM is seeking applicants from around 35 disciplines, including civil, structural, mechanical, electrical, building services, fire and sustainable buildings engineering, as well as quantity & building surveying, project management, planning & design, acoustics, water & power related disciplines, and environment including remediation, EIA, ecology, air quality, GIS, and much more.

GRADUATE VACANCIES IN 2024

CONSULTING
ENGINEERING
PROPERTY
TECHNOLOGY

NUMBER OF VACANCIES
350-400 graduate jobs

LOCATIONS OF VACANCIES

Vacancies also available in Europe.

STARTING SALARY FOR 2024
£28,500-£32,500

WORK EXPERIENCE

| DEGREE PLACEMENTS | SUMMER INTERNSHIPS |

UNIVERSITY PROMOTIONS DURING 2023-2024
ABERDEEN, ASTON, BATH, BELFAST, BIRMINGHAM, BRISTOL, CAMBRIDGE, CARDIFF, CITY, DUNDEE, DURHAM, EDINBURGH, EXETER, GLASGOW, HERIOT-WATT, IMPERIAL COLLEGE LONDON, LEEDS, LEICESTER, LIVERPOOL, LOUGHBOROUGH, MANCHESTER, NEWCASTLE, NORTHUMBRIA, NOTTINGHAM, NOTTINGHAM TRENT, OXFORD BROOKES, PLYMOUTH, READING, SHEFFIELD, SOUTHAMPTON, STRATHCLYDE, SURREY, ULSTER, UNIVERSITY COLLEGE LONDON, WARWICK, YORK

MINIMUM ENTRY REQUIREMENTS
2.1 Degree

APPLICATION DEADLINE
Year-round recruitment
Early application is advised.

FURTHER INFORMATION
www.Top100GraduateEmployers.com
Register now for the latest news, local promotions, work experience and graduate vacancies at AECOM.

AECOM
I improve the energy performance of listed buildings
Meet Katie,
an engineering graduate at AECOM who is using building performance analysis software and energy models to inform different design options to improve the performance of listed buildings.
Find out how you can make an impact at
aecom.com/uk/impact
Delivering a better world

AIRBUS

Airbus is at the forefront of innovating new technologies, with a pioneering spirit that has redefined the aerospace industry. Its products bring people closer together. Airbus strives to continually push the boundaries of what is possible to safeguard the world for future generations.

Every year Airbus looks for graduates from around the world to join them. Airbus needs people with the aspiration, enthusiasm, and the talent to move the aerospace industry forward – to deliver their vision, and to pioneer sustainable aerospace for a safe and united world. With roles available across the UK, Europe and around the world – the graduate programme at Airbus is truly global.

The graduate programme at Airbus helps graduates take flight with their career, joining a development pathway that will assist graduates personal and professional growth. Graduates will be part of a global community that come together on a regular basis to meet peers, hear from leaders, and learn from the industry's best talents.

Over the course of the programme graduates can also gain experience through a series of rotational placements. The placements are tailored to suit each graduate's needs, as well as those of the business, encouraging individuals to take control of their own career and to explore the different business functions at Airbus. Airbus has opportunities across all of its divisions in a multitude of functions – Engineering, Finance, Marketing, Customer Support, Procurement – to name but a few!

What's more, working alongside passionate and determined people, Airbus graduates will help to accomplish the extraordinary – on the ground, in the sky, and in space.

GRADUATE VACANCIES IN 2024

ENGINEERING

FINANCE

LOGISTICS

MARKETING

PURCHASING

RESEARCH & DEVELOPMENT

TECHNOLOGY

NUMBER OF VACANCIES
150+ graduate jobs

LOCATIONS OF VACANCIES

Vacancies also available in Europe, the USA and Asia.

STARTING SALARY FOR 2024
£31,000
Plus profit sharing, relocation, and employee share plans.

WORK EXPERIENCE
DEGREE
PLACEMENTS

UNIVERSITY PROMOTIONS DURING 2023-2024
BATH, IMPERIAL COLLEGE LONDON, LIVERPOOL, LOUGHBOROUGH, MANCHESTER, SHEFFIELD
Please check with your university careers service for full details of Airbus' local promotions and events.

MINIMUM ENTRY REQUIREMENTS
Varies by function
Relevant degree required for some roles.

APPLICATION DEADLINE
Varies by function

FURTHER INFORMATION
www.Top100GraduateEmployers.com
Register now for the latest news, local promotions, work experience and graduate vacancies at Airbus.

Arriving in the UK back in 1990, Aldi is now one of the fastest growing supermarkets. Just like their business growth, Graduate Area Managers will progress at pace. Across 12 months, exceptional training will steer graduates on their way to managing their own £multi-million business.

There are many reasons to join the Graduate Area Manager programme: the responsibility, the development, the support, and yes, the £50,000 starting salary and a fully expensed company car. But top of the list should be the opportunity to get involved, give more – and get even more back! Within the first 12 months, graduates will become responsible for a portfolio of stores, experiencing a dynamic retail environment that will sharpen their commercial edge and equip them with the skills to make business critical decisions. It's the perfect introduction to Aldi and a superb foundation for future success.

Depending on business needs, graduates with the willingness and drive to be flexible in both their areas of responsibility and location may get the chance to take on a project role within our Stores, Warehouse or National departments, or even on an International Secondment.

Beyond that, high-performing Area Managers could even progress to a Directorship role. Don't shop around – with enthusiasm and ambition, this is the chance to become a future leader at Aldi.

The key to Aldi's success is the people – without them, it wouldn't be possible. It's a business with integrity – fair to partners and suppliers, and everything it does is for the benefit of customers, colleagues and the community – whether that's through lowering the cost of groceries for millions of customers, supporting British suppliers or taking steps to create an inclusive workplace for everyone in Team Aldi. Simply put, Aldi means more.

GRADUATE VACANCIES IN 2024
GENERAL MANAGEMENT
RETAIL

NUMBER OF VACANCIES
100 graduate jobs

LOCATIONS OF VACANCIES

STARTING SALARY FOR 2024
£50,000

WORK EXPERIENCE
DEGREE
PLACEMENTS

UNIVERSITY PROMOTIONS DURING 2023-2024
ABERDEEN, ABERYSTWYTH, ASTON, BANGOR, BATH, BIRMINGHAM, BRADFORD, BRISTOL, BRUNEL, CAMBRIDGE, CARDIFF, CITY, DUNDEE, DURHAM, EDINBURGH, ESSEX, EXETER, GLASGOW, HERIOT-WATT, HULL, IMPERIAL COLLEGE LONDON, KEELE, KING'S COLLEGE LONDON, KENT, LANCASTER, LEEDS, LEICESTER, LIVERPOOL, LONDON SCHOOL OF ECONOMICS, LOUGHBOROUGH, MANCHESTER, NEWCASTLE, NORTHUMBRIA, NOTTINGHAM, NOTTINGHAM TRENT, OXFORD, OXFORD BROOKES, PLYMOUTH, QUEEN MARY LONDON, READING, ROYAL HOLLOWAY, SCHOOL OF AFRICAN STUDIES, SHEFFIELD, SOUTHAMPTON, ST ANDREWS, STIRLING, STRATHCLYDE, SURREY, SUSSEX, SWANSEA, UEA, ULSTER, UNIVERSITY COLLEGE LONDON, WARWICK, YORK

MINIMUM ENTRY REQUIREMENTS
2.1 Degree

APPLICATION DEADLINE
Year-round recruitment
Early application is advised.

FURTHER INFORMATION
www.Top100GraduateEmployers.com
Register now for the latest news, local promotions, work experience and graduate vacancies at Aldi.

Amazon's mission is to be Earth's most customer-centric company. This is what unites Amazonians across teams and geographies as they are all striving to delight customers and make their lives easier, one innovative product, service, and idea at a time.

Every year, Amazon offers hundreds of graduates the opportunity to design their path to a successful career. Starting from Day 1, graduates are given a leadership position with significant responsibilities. Amazon believes in hiring and developing the best; their graduates are given numerous opportunities to acquire technical skills that will enable them to take on future opportunities within the company. By working on behalf of its customers, Amazon is building the future – one innovative product, service and idea at a time.

Amazon encourages graduates to have a self-starter mentality when it comes to learning, and they supplement this with hands-on training to enable their people to progress and succeed.

There are opportunities across a broad spectrum of teams, and many graduates join the organisation as Area Managers, who lead and develop teams. Amazon hires the brightest minds and offers them the platform to think around corners and innovate on behalf of their customers.

Amazon is a company of builders who bring varying backgrounds, ideas, and points of view to inventing on behalf of their customers. Amazon's diverse perspectives come from many sources including gender, race, age, national origin, sexual orientation, culture, education, and professional and life experience.

Amazon is committed to diversity and inclusion and always look for ways to scale their impact as they grow.

GRADUATE VACANCIES IN 2024

ENGINEERING
FINANCE
GENERAL MANAGEMENT
HUMAN RESOURCES
LOGISTICS

NUMBER OF VACANCIES
200 graduate jobs

LOCATIONS OF VACANCIES

Vacancies also available in Europe.

STARTING SALARY FOR 2024
£28,000-£36,000
Plus relocation allowance, sign-on and RSU bonuses.

WORK EXPERIENCE
SUMMER
INTERNSHIPS

UNIVERSITY PROMOTIONS DURING 2023-2024
ASTON, BATH, BIRMINGHAM, BRISTOL, CAMBRIDGE, CARDIFF, CITY, DURHAM, EDINBURGH, EXETER, GLASGOW, IMPERIAL COLLEGE LONDON, KING'S COLLEGE LONDON, LANCASTER, LEEDS, LEICESTER, LIVERPOOL, LONDON SCHOOL OF ECONOMICS, LOUGHBOROUGH, MANCHESTER, NEWCASTLE, NOTTINGHAM, OXFORD, QUEEN MARY LONDON, READING, SHEFFIELD, SOUTHAMPTON, ST ANDREWS, STRATHCLYDE, SWANSEA, UNIVERSITY COLLEGE LONDON, WARWICK, YORK

MINIMUM ENTRY REQUIREMENTS
Any degree accepted

APPLICATION DEADLINE
Year-round recruitment
Early application is advised.

FURTHER INFORMATION
www.Top100GraduateEmployers.com
Register now for the latest news, local promotions, work experience and graduate vacancies at Amazon.

We are hiring Graduates and Interns

Are you a recent or upcoming graduate looking to launch an exceptional career with a focus on expanding your leadership skills?

Amazon is hiring thousands of Business Analyst, Finance, Health & Safety, HR, Loss Prevention, Operations, and Project Management leaders to join the Operations team in support of our global fulfilment, sortation and delivery network.

Come build the future with us

SCAN ME FOR
CORPORATE ROLES

SCAN ME FOR
OPERATIONS ROLES

AON

aon.com/careers/early-careers/uk

Aonplc **f** graduates@aon.co.uk ✕

@Aon_plc **y** linkedin.com/company/aon **in**

Aon exists to shape decisions for the better – to protect and enrich the lives of people around the world. Their 50,000 colleagues provide clients in over 120 countries and sovereignties with advice and solutions that give them clarity and confidence to make better decisions.

Aon believes that businesses thrive when the communities they serve and the people they employ also flourish. At Aon, their people are the heartbeat of their firm. They have a passion for bringing the best to their clients, which unites them and drives them as a global firm.

Depending on the area of Aon that they join, graduates will use their analytical capabilities, commercial awareness, and communication skills to help clients address the key questions that affect their businesses. How will the rise of inflation and cost of living affect the ability to conduct business and bring goods to the people who need them? How could the collapse of the Eurozone affect the world economy? What could climate change mean to Europe? Aon's business is to provide the answers to help clients make better decisions.

Graduates join Aon across a range of consulting and broking roles within business areas including actuarial analysis, investment, insurance and reinsurance, insurance strategy, employee benefits, reward and remuneration, talent and employee engagement and cybersecurity.

Aon's Launch development programme is designed to support and develop the future stars of the business by helping graduates build their business acumen and engage in strengthening relationships with clients and colleagues. In addition to technical training, colleagues are fully supported in allocating time to study for relevant professional qualifications to enable them to have a greater impact on Aon's clients and confidently progress within their chosen career path.

GRADUATE VACANCIES IN 2024

CONSULTING

FINANCE

TECHNOLOGY

NUMBER OF VACANCIES
200 graduate jobs

LOCATIONS OF VACANCIES

Vacancies also available worldwide.

STARTING SALARY FOR 2024
£Competitive

WORK EXPERIENCE

DEGREE PLACEMENTS   SUMMER INTERNSHIPS

**UNIVERSITY PROMOTIONS
DURING 2023-2024**
BATH, BIRMINGHAM, BRISTOL, CITY,
DURHAM, ESSEX, GLASGOW, HERIOT-WATT,
IMPERIAL COLLEGE LONDON, KENT,
LEEDS, LONDON SCHOOL OF ECONOMICS,
LOUGHBOROUGH, MANCHESTER,
NOTTINGHAM, QUEEN MARY LONDON,
UNIVERSITY COLLEGE LONDON, WARWICK
*Please check with your university careers
service for full details of Aon's local
promotions and events.*

MINIMUM ENTRY REQUIREMENTS
2.1 Degree

APPLICATION DEADLINE
Varies by function

FURTHER INFORMATION
www.Top100GraduateEmployers.com
*Register now for the latest news, local
promotions, work experience and
graduate vacancies at Aon.*

AON

Grow your career from day one

Whether you're interested in a graduate programme, internship, industrial placement or apprenticeship, Aon has the right early careers programme for you.

**Visit our website to learn more at
aon.com/careers/early-careers/uk**

#AonEarlyCareers

aon.com

Arcadis is the world's leading company delivering sustainable design, engineering and consultancy solutions for natural and built assets. Right now, more than 36,000 Arcadians in over 70 countries are working to address the world's challenges, such as climate change, urbanisation, digitalisation and poverty.

Arcadis' story began back in 1888 in the Netherlands, where they developed unusable land into places for people to live and establish communities. Nowadays, they focus on creating better housing, revolutionising transport systems and finding new solutions to complex environmental challenges. Arcadis embeds sustainability across everything they do to deliver solutions that are resilient, effective and within planetary boundaries.

The future of Arcadis is being shaped by the mindset of its people. That is why they constantly seek fresh and diverse thinkers who are problem-solvers for the planet, bringing new perspectives and fresh ways of thinking.

The Arcadis Graduate GROW programme is a structured 3-year programme, designed to help graduates evolve and develop skills to help them to become an experienced professional in their chosen field. Arcadis' graduates are supported from day one with structured training, mentoring, as well as support for gaining industry accreditations.

Arcadis' "People First" culture propelled the company to become one of The Sunday Times' Best Places to Work in the UK in 2023. They are committed to providing an innovative and healthy work environment for Arcadians where flexibility, sustainability, diversity and inclusion, as well as charitable works sit at the core.

At Arcadis, graduates can create a lasting legacy and make a mark on their lives and the world around them.

GRADUATE VACANCIES IN 2024

CONSULTING
ENGINEERING

NUMBER OF VACANCIES
200 graduate jobs

LOCATIONS OF VACANCIES

STARTING SALARY FOR 2024
£25,250-£34,000

WORK EXPERIENCE

DEGREE PLACEMENTS | SUMMER INTERNSHIPS

UNIVERSITY PROMOTIONS DURING 2023-2024
ASTON, BATH, BIRMINGHAM, BRISTOL, CARDIFF, EDINBURGH, EXETER, GLASGOW, LEEDS, LOUGHBOROUGH, MANCHESTER, NOTTINGHAM TRENT, OXFORD BROOKES, PLYMOUTH, READING, SHEFFIELD, SOUTHAMPTON, ULSTER, UNIVERSITY COLLEGE LONDON
Please check with your university careers service for full details of Arcadis' local promotions and events.

MINIMUM ENTRY REQUIREMENTS
2.2 Degree

APPLICATION DEADLINE
Varies by function

FURTHER INFORMATION
www.Top100GraduateEmployers.com
*Register now for the latest news, local promotions, work experience and graduate vacancies at **Arcadis**.*

We'll help you grow.

Personally and professionally

We constantly seek fresh thinkers who are problem-solvers for the planet and share our passion in improving quality of life.

Join Arcadis. Create a legacy.

ARCADIS

Create a legacy at Arcadis

careers.arcadis.com

@AstraZeneca 🐦   AstraZeneca f
linkedin.com/company/astrazeneca 🔗
@AstraZeneca 📷   youtube.com/astrazeneca ▶

AstraZeneca is a global, science-led, patient-focused pharmaceutical company employing 100,000 people worldwide. They are dedicated to transforming the future of healthcare by unlocking the power of what science can do for people, society and the planet.

AstraZeneca's graduate programmes offer huge variety when it comes to graduate learning and potential for growth.

Graduates are empowered to jump in, take the initiative, be part of meaningful project teams, and make an impact by delivering real value to patients and business. Their programmes place an emphasis on personal and professional development, and invest in each graduate's unique interests and potential.

Working in a fast-paced, yet deeply supportive and collaborative environment, graduates are encouraged to take responsibility and put their knowledge into practice, whilst being supported by inspiring peers. AstraZeneca's graduates work hard, building a rich and supportive network that will last a lifetime. Graduates have significant opportunities to build bonds with their international peers, developing connections and growing their network with experts and leaders across the business.

Programmes bring diverse talent from all over the world together to gain an international perspective and combine strengths and knowledge to multiply impact. AstraZeneca is proud of their award-winning, progressive working practices. They welcome diverse thinking, curiosity, collaboration and the courage to go further, together.

To find out more about becoming a part of their team, visit the early talent pages of their global careers site.

GRADUATE VACANCIES IN 2024
ENGINEERING
FINANCE
GENERAL MANAGEMENT
LOGISTICS
MARKETING
RESEARCH & DEVELOPMENT
SALES
TECHNOLOGY

NUMBER OF VACANCIES
100+ graduate jobs

LOCATIONS OF VACANCIES

Vacancies also available in Europe, the USA and Asia.

STARTING SALARY FOR 2024
£32,000+
Plus benefits fund, bonus and relocation (if applicable).

WORK EXPERIENCE
DEGREE PLACEMENTS   SUMMER INTERNSHIPS

UNIVERSITY PROMOTIONS DURING 2023-2024
BATH, BIRMINGHAM, BRISTOL, BRUNEL, CARDIFF, EDINBURGH, GLASGOW, IMPERIAL COLLEGE LONDON, KING'S COLLEGE LONDON, LEEDS, LEICESTER, LIVERPOOL, MANCHESTER, NOTTINGHAM, OXFORD, QUEEN MARY LONDON, SHEFFIELD, SOUTHAMPTON, UNIVERSITY COLLEGE LONDON, WARWICK, YORK

MINIMUM ENTRY REQUIREMENTS
Varies by function
Relevant degree required for some roles.

APPLICATION DEADLINE
Varies by function

FURTHER INFORMATION
www.Top100GraduateEmployers.com
Register now for the latest news, local promotions, work experience and graduate vacancies at AstraZeneca.

Make an impact and kickstart your career

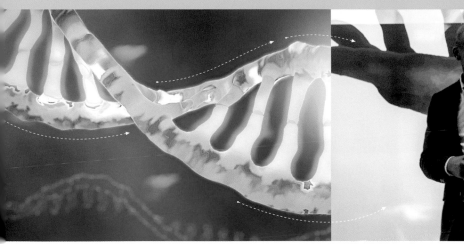

We have exciting and rewarding Graduate Programmes in:

- Biometrics & Information Sciences
- BioPharmaceutical Development
- Commercial, Marketing & Market Access
- Data Sciences & Artificial Intelligence
- Finance
- Innovation & Business Excellence
- IT/Technology Leadership
- Medical
- Operations & Supply Chain
- Patient Safety
- Pharmaceutical Technology & Development
- Precision Medicines
- Research & Development

Starting salary for 2024

£32,000+

Plus bonus, benefits
& relocation (if applicable)

For more information and to apply, please visit:
careers.astrazeneca.com/early-talent

BAE SYSTEMS

gart@baesystems.com

@LifeBAESystems   LifeatBAESystems

@LifeatBAESystems   linkedin.com/company/bae-systems

BAE Systems helps to protect people and national security, critical infrastructure and vital information. It's a culture that values diversity, rewards integrity and merit, and is a place where everyone has the opportunity to fulfil their potential, no matter what their background.

With a workforce of 90,500 people in more than 40 counties, BAE systems is committed to nurturing talent and striving for excellence; empowering their people to drive innovation, make the right decisions and solve complex challenges.

BAE Systems is a place graduates and undergraduates can start, and grow, their career with confidence. From engineering, to project management, technology, manufacturing, consultancy, and finance or wider business disciplines, graduates have the chance to make a real impact from day one. With opportunities nationwide, joining a BAE Systems programme means working, and learning, alongside the brightest minds.

Graduates have the ability to pace their own programme journey, from 18 to 30 months, to match their career aspirations and personal ambitions – and on completion, could even find themselves on BAE Systems' Future Talent Programme.

BAE Systems is committed to working to high ethical and environmental standards – it's an inclusive, collaborative culture where everyone has the chance to build a varied career and is empowered to achieve their potential and be themselves.

Be part of a collaborative culture creating the next generation of security products and services. Embrace the opportunity to make a difference – apply now.

GRADUATE VACANCIES IN 2024

ACCOUNTANCY
CONSULTING
ENGINEERING
FINANCE
GENERAL MANAGEMENT
HUMAN RESOURCES
MARKETING
SALES
TECHNOLOGY

NUMBER OF VACANCIES
800 graduate jobs

LOCATIONS OF VACANCIES

STARTING SALARY FOR 2024
£34,000
Plus a £2,000 bonus.

WORK EXPERIENCE

DEGREE PLACEMENTS   SUMMER INTERNSHIPS

UNIVERSITY PROMOTIONS DURING 2023-2024
ASTON, BATH, BIRMINGHAM, BRISTOL, CAMBRIDGE, CARDIFF, CRANFIELD, DURHAM, EDINBURGH, EXETER, GLASGOW, IMPERIAL COLLEGE LONDON, KENT, LANCASTER, LEEDS, LEICESTER, LIVERPOOL, LIVERPOOL JOHN MOORES, LOUGHBOROUGH, MANCHESTER, NEWCASTLE, NOTTINGHAM, NOTTINGHAM TRENT, OXFORD, PLYMOUTH, PORTSMOUTH, QUEEN MARY LONDON, SHEFFIELD, SOUTHAMPTON, STRATHCLYDE, SURREY, UNIVERSITY COLLEGE LONDON, UNIVERSITY OF CENTRAL LANCASHIRE, WARWICK, YORK

MINIMUM ENTRY REQUIREMENTS
Varies by function
Relevant degree required for some roles.

APPLICATION DEADLINE
Varies by function

FURTHER INFORMATION
www.Top100GraduateEmployers.com
Register now for the latest news, local promotions, work experience and graduate vacancies at BAE Systems.

Welcome to a career where everyone can make a difference

baesystems.com/graduates

Our graduates come from all walks of life, but they are united by one thing - talent.

With your unique skills and experiences, you'll play an important role in creating a secure tomorrow for generations to come.

When you join a BAE Systems graduate programme, you'll have access to the training, development and opportunities you need to make sure your talent shines.

From engineering, project management, or technology, to manufacturing, consulting or finance - whichever role you choose, you'll be empowered to be your best in a supportive culture where your hard work will be recognised and your contribution valued.

Everyone's welcome. We're committed to recruiting the best and most diverse talent to our team, bringing your unique insights and perspectives to build a better tomorrow.

Join us - this is the place where you can make a real difference.
baesystems.com/graduates

90,500
Employees worldwide

£34,000
Starting salary
+£2,000 bonus

+£105m
Invested annually
in education and skills

4 Intakes in January, April
May and September

#2
Engineering Employer
of Choice as voted for
by female engineering
job hunters in the
UK Graduate Careers
Survey 2023

+40
Countries

+50
UK sites

+1300
Graduate and
undergraduate
opportunities in 2024

Follow **Life at BAE Systems**

BAE SYSTEMS

BANK OF AMERICA

Bank of America knows being a great place to work for its employees is core to their success. While their teammates are focused on supporting clients and communities, Bank of America are focused on supporting teammates and their families, making sure they can be their best both at work and at home.

Bank of America welcomes graduates from all universities, degrees and backgrounds into its diverse and inclusive workplace. They firmly believe all employees should be treated with respect and be able to bring their whole selves to work. This is core to who they are as a company and how they drive responsible growth. Graduates can join Bank of America in areas including Audit, Research, Risk, Sales & Trading, Technology and more.

Each line of business offers unique opportunities, and there's plenty of collaboration across the bank designed to shape a smarter, greener, safer and more inclusive world. This includes everything from helping clients achieve sustainable growth and working with external partners to increase the number of women working in tech. As well as getting involved in exciting client projects, graduates are encouraged to make the most of the various internal groups and events such as sport and social club activities, employee network events and volunteering programmes.

Bank of America is committed to improving the environment in how they approach their global business strategy, work with partners, make their operations more sustainable, support their employees, manage risks and govern their activities. All of these opportunities give teammates the chance to shape a meaningful career, build connections both within and outside the bank and spend time on what matters to them.

Discover careers at Bank of America today.

GRADUATE VACANCIES IN 2024

ACCOUNTANCY
FINANCE
INVESTMENT BANKING
TECHNOLOGY

NUMBER OF VACANCIES
No fixed quota

LOCATIONS OF VACANCIES

Vacancies also available in Europe.

STARTING SALARY FOR 2024
£Competitive

WORK EXPERIENCE

INSIGHT COURSES | DEGREE PLACEMENTS | SUMMER INTERNSHIPS

UNIVERSITY PROMOTIONS DURING 2023-2024
BANGOR, BATH, BIRMINGHAM, BRISTOL, CAMBRIDGE, DURHAM, EDINBURGH, IMPERIAL COLLEGE LONDON, KING'S COLLEGE LONDON, LANCASTER, LEEDS, LIVERPOOL, LONDON SCHOOL OF ECONOMICS, MANCHESTER, NOTTINGHAM, OXFORD, QUEEN MARY LONDON, SOUTHAMPTON, SURREY, UNIVERSITY COLLEGE LONDON, WARWICK, YORK
Please check with your university careers service for full details of Bank of America's local promotions and events.

MINIMUM ENTRY REQUIREMENTS
2.1 Degree

APPLICATION DEADLINE
Varies by function

FURTHER INFORMATION
www.Top100GraduateEmployers.com
*Register now for the latest news, local promotions, work experience and graduate vacancies at **Bank of America**.*

How would you shape your world?

All of our internships, placements and programs offer training, development and support. We'll help you learn, grow and belong while you begin a career with global impact.

Here at Bank of America, you'll be supported to succeed through mentorship programs and development opportunities. We foster a diverse, inclusive culture, where you'll build networks and find friendships. You'll be given real responsibilities, develop skills for the future, and discover which areas of our business most appeal to you.

campus.bankofamerica.com

@BofA_Careers

BANK OF AMERICA

Barclays is a British universal bank, diversified by business, by different types of customers and clients, and by geography. Barclays' global businesses include consumer banking and payments operations, as well as a top-tier, full service corporate and investment bank with a heritage of success.

Joining Barclays as a graduate or intern means the opportunity to do truly meaningful work, to discover a financial company that's focused on a better future for everyone, and to develop skills that will pave the way for a career that's both challenging and inspiring.

Spanning everything from Technology to Investment Banking, Barclays' two global graduate programmes will either develop graduates into a technical expert in their chosen field or help to build an extraordinary depth and breadth of experience through a deep dive into a chosen business area. Meanwhile, interns at the bank are immersed in real projects with real outcomes.

At Barclays, graduates and interns help to shape the future. The bank has a legacy of innovation, from introducing the first ATMs to launching contactless payments. Today, that forward-thinking approach continues. Barclays is committed to being a net zero bank by 2050, for example, and is experimenting with emerging technologies like blockchain and quantum computing.

Those joining can expect immediate responsibility, exciting collaborations, and ongoing training. This means Barclays looks for graduates with an innate sense of curiosity, along with the agility and adaptability it takes to come up with new ideas that can become ground-breaking.

With an inclusive culture, Barclays welcomes people from all walks of life. Whoever graduates are and wherever they want to get to, there really are no limits as to what they can do, what they can discover, and how fast they develop.

GRADUATE VACANCIES IN 2024

ENGINEERING

FINANCE

HUMAN RESOURCES

INVESTMENT BANKING

MARKETING

RESEARCH & DEVELOPMENT

SALES

TECHNOLOGY

NUMBER OF VACANCIES
900+ graduate jobs

LOCATIONS OF VACANCIES

STARTING SALARY FOR 2024
£Competitive
Graduates receive scholarship and bursary payment.

WORK EXPERIENCE

| INSIGHT COURSES | DEGREE PLACEMENTS | SUMMER INTERNSHIPS |

UNIVERSITY PROMOTIONS DURING 2023-2024
ABERDEEN, ASTON, BIRMINGHAM, BIRMINGHAM CITY, BRUNEL, CHESTER, CRANFIELD, DUNDEE, DURHAM, EDGE HILL UNIVERSITY, EDINBURGH, EDINBURGH NAPIER, EXETER, GLASGOW, GLASGOW CALEDONIAN, GREENWICH, HERIOT-WATT, IMPERIAL COLLEGE LONDON, KING'S COLLEGE LONDON, LANCASTER, LEICESTER, LIVERPOOL JOHN MOORES, MANCHESTER, MANCHESTER METROPOLITAN, NORTHAMPTON, NOTTINGHAM, NOTTINGHAM TRENT, SALFORD, ST ANDREWS, STIRLING, STRATHCLYDE, THE UNIVERSITY OF THE WEST OF SCOTLAND, UNIVERSITY COLLEGE LONDON, WARWICK

APPLICATION DEADLINE
Varies by function

FURTHER INFORMATION
www.Top100GraduateEmployers.com
*Register now for the latest news, local promotions, work experience and graduate vacancies at **Barclays**.*

DO, DISCOVER, DEVELOP.

Join Barclays as a graduate or intern, and you'll do work that challenges you, discover opportunities to stretch you and develop innovations that excite you. You'll enjoy the kind of training that will bring out the best in you. And you'll be empowered to discover your full potential.

To find out more, type search.jobs.barclays

 **BARCLAYS**

B B C

The BBC is the world's leading public service broadcaster, producing distinctive, world-class programmes and content which inform, educate, and entertain millions of people in the UK and around the world. More than 20,000 staff work at the BBC in journalism, production, engineering, technology, and corporate services.

The BBC delivers content across the UK through a portfolio of television services, national and local radio networks, BBC World Service and a range of digital services.

With a strong focus on potential rather than the level of academic achievement, the BBC has graduate and postgraduate-level apprenticeship and trainee schemes across the board in Journalism, Content Engineering, Software Engineering, Research and Development, UX Design, Marketing, Business and Law.

BBC schemes include a mix of on-the-job learning and in many cases academic study, giving successful applicants the opportunity to gain a qualification.

New perspectives are important to the BBC, as is motivation for the role, a positive attitude and an appetite for curiosity. Evidence of good communication skills, team working and creativity will strengthen applications.

The BBC's graduate apprenticeship schemes for 2024 are expected to open for applications from Autumn 2023, with assessment centres taking place in early 2024 for a September start.

To see all opportunities available at the BBC throughout the year, interested students should register on the BBC's careers site and follow them on social media to keep up-to-date with scheme opening dates.

GRADUATE VACANCIES IN 2024
ENGINEERING
FINANCE
HUMAN RESOURCES
LAW
MARKETING
MEDIA
RESEARCH & DEVELOPMENT
TECHNOLOGY

NUMBER OF VACANCIES
200+ graduate jobs

LOCATIONS OF VACANCIES

STARTING SALARY FOR 2024
£20,475-£25,000

WORK EXPERIENCE
INTERNSHIPS PLACEMENTS

UNIVERSITY PROMOTIONS DURING 2023-2024
Please check with your university careers service for full details of the BBC's local promotions and events.

MINIMUM ENTRY REQUIREMENTS
Varies by scheme

APPLICATION DEADLINE
Varies by scheme

FURTHER INFORMATION
www.Top100GraduateEmployers.com
Register now for the latest news, local promotions, work experience and graduate vacancies at the BBC.

Be part of something special. Join the BBC.

Opportunities in Broadcast Engineering, Software Engineering, Research & Development, User Experience, Journalism, Production and more.

To find out more, visit careers.bbc.co.uk

BCG

When organisations find problems they can't solve on their own, that's where BCG gets to work. As the pioneer in business strategy consulting, it has been helping to solve some of the world's biggest problems since it was founded nearly 60 years ago. Today, its work is more fascinating than ever.

Graduates will join a 22,000-strong global team of consultants and subject-matter experts to partner with global clients on projects that make positive change happen. BCG helps organisations flourish in a world where sustainability is the priority. To date, BCG has enabled almost £2 billion in social impact consulting, and has made its own pledge to achieve net-zero climate impact by 2030.

Working at BCG, graduates will start making an impact on day one, with early exposure to the most senior leaders of global corporations. There are opportunities to build experience across different industries and sectors, and to work in projects at the forefront of technology, like advanced robotics, artificial intelligence, and blockchain.

This focus on the future means that BCG offers unparalleled opportunities for growth and development. The firm never stops learning: it continually invests in its employees with in-depth learning experiences, curated and led by senior BCGers and top-tier trainers from around the world.

BCG looks for bright students from any subject matter or discipline. It values people with high academic achievement, leadership skills, deep intellectual curiosity, and a problem-solving mindset. Diversity of thought, expertise, experience, and background are fundamental to BCG's success.

For graduates looking to continue their learning journey and make a real difference in the world, BCG is the place to start.

GRADUATE VACANCIES IN 2024

CONSULTING

NUMBER OF VACANCIES
No fixed quota

LOCATIONS OF VACANCIES

STARTING SALARY FOR 2024
£Competitive
Competitive compensation and benefits package including an annual discretionary performance related bonus.

WORK EXPERIENCE
INSIGHT COURSES | SUMMER INTERNSHIPS

UNIVERSITY PROMOTIONS DURING 2023-2024
BATH, BIRMINGHAM, BRISTOL, CAMBRIDGE, CARDIFF, DURHAM, EDINBURGH, EXETER, GLASGOW, IMPERIAL COLLEGE LONDON, KING'S COLLEGE LONDON, LEEDS, LIVERPOOL, LONDON SCHOOL OF ECONOMICS, MANCHESTER, NEWCASTLE, NOTTINGHAM, OXFORD, SCHOOL OF AFRICAN STUDIES, SHEFFIELD, SOUTHAMPTON, ST ANDREWS, UNIVERSITY COLLEGE LONDON, WARWICK, YORK

MINIMUM ENTRY REQUIREMENTS
2.1 Degree

APPLICATION DEADLINE
26th October 2023

FURTHER INFORMATION
www.Top100GraduateEmployers.com
Register now for the latest news, local promotions, work experience and graduate vacancies at BCG.

Felix, Nick and Ashna, London

Beyond growth.

We're dedicated to your success with deep career development and networking opportunities. Based on our own employees' ratings, Comparably ranked us as the #1 company for career growth in 2022 and 2023.

Scan Here

careers.bcg.com

Beyond is where we begin. | **BCG**

earlyincareer@bdo.co.uk

linkedin.com/company/bdo-llp

@LifeatBDO youtube.com/bdollp

Accountancy and business advisory firm, BDO employs over 7000 people across 18 offices in the UK, providing the solutions ambitious and entrepreneurial businesses need to navigate today's changing world. BDO UK is part of the BDO global network, providing advisory services in 164 countries.

When the most innovative and high-growth businesses need advice on accountancy and business, they turn to BDO. With expertise across Financial Services, Healthcare, Leisure and Hospitality, Retail, Manufacturing, Technology, Media, Not-for-Profit, Public Sector and many more industries, BDO provides the advice and answers that help AIM listed companies achieve their aspirations. Specialising in Tax, Audit & Assurance and Advisory, BDO's graduate programmes are for those who want to work with ambitious clients, on challenging work, from day one.

They look for trainees who want to bring themselves to everything they do. Those who are prepared to ask questions, offer up ideas and seize every opportunity. Those who have a drive to inspire more conversations and build lasting relationships. And in return, BDO will provide a breadth of experience and opportunities to develop skills that few could match.

Study for professional qualifications like the ACA, CFA and CTA to become an expert in a chosen area. At BDO, trainees are shaped into the independent and ethical advisors the UK's most forward-thinking businesses rely on. With early exposure to clients, trainees experience varied work that will broaden their horizons. BDO provides expert coaching and mentoring at every step, so that trainees can build a career with confidence.

Want to work at the very heart of accountancy and business?

Set a course for a rewarding career, with a role at BDO.

GRADUATE VACANCIES IN 2024

ACCOUNTANCY

NUMBER OF VACANCIES
620 graduate jobs

LOCATIONS OF VACANCIES

STARTING SALARY FOR 2024
£Competitive
Varies by region.

WORK EXPERIENCE

DEGREE PLACEMENTS | SUMMER INTERNSHIPS

UNIVERSITY PROMOTIONS DURING 2023-2024
BIRMINGHAM, COVENTRY, DURHAM, EAST ANGLIA, EDINBURGH, ESSEX, EXETER, GLASGOW, KING'S COLLEGE LONDON, LEEDS, LIVERPOOL, LIVERPOOL JOHN MOORES, LONDON SCHOOL OF ECONOMICS, LOUGHBOROUGH, MANCHESTER, NEWCASTLE, NOTTINGHAM, NOTTINGHAM TRENT, QUEEN MARY LONDON, READING, SHEFFIELD HALLAM, SOUTHAMPTON, STRATHCLYDE, SURREY, SUSSEX, UNIVERSITY COLLEGE LONDON, WARWICK, YORK
Please check with your university careers service for full details of BDO's local promotions and events.

MINIMUM ENTRY REQUIREMENTS
Any degree accepted

APPLICATION DEADLINE
November 2023
Programmes will open for applications in September. Early application is advised.

FURTHER INFORMATION
www.Top100GraduateEmployers.com
Register now for the latest news, local promotions, work experience and graduate vacancies at BDO.

IDEAS | PEOPLE | TRUST

FROM **STARTING** A NEW **CHAPTER**

TO **WRITING** YOUR **OWN** **STORY**

Graduate programmes at BDO.

From asking questions to growing your expertise, from finding your feet to stepping up. At BDO, we'll be with you every step of the way as you start your exciting journey in the world of accountancy.

On our graduate programme, you'll experience real responsibility and purpose from day one. Working with people who value your ideas and invest in your success, you'll be helping to solve complex business challenges while earning a respected qualification at the same time. And with exposure to a range of industries across the UK and beyond, you'll build a powerful network that will boost your personal and professional growth — all with the support of a friendly and welcoming team around you.

This is where it all begins.
Start your journey at **careers.bdo.co.uk**

BlackRock

BlackRock's purpose is to help more and more people experience financial well-being. As a global investment manager and leading provider of financial technology, their clients turn to them for the solutions needed when planning for their most important goals.

BlackRock is building a culture of innovation, curiosity and compassion, one that enables every employee to make an impact. Being a part of BlackRock means being a part of a community of smart, ambitious people. BlackRock values diversity of thought and background and believes everyone should have a voice at the table. No matter what level, employees are given real responsibility from day one – and BlackRock is looking for future colleagues to help challenge the status quo. BlackRock brings together financial leadership, worldwide reach and state-of-the-art technology to provide answers to the millions of investors who entrust their financial futures to the company.

The story of BlackRock's success rests not just with its founders, but with the thousands of talented people who have brought their ideas and energy to the firm every day since. That's why BlackRock is looking for fresh ideas and viewpoints. BlackRock knows that their continued success depends on their ability to use collective experiences and ideas to achieve more for their clients and the business. At BlackRock, students can have a career that's exciting, rewarding and full of possibilities and opportunities.

BlackRock offers roles in Analytics and Risk; Business Management and Strategy; Business Operations; Finance and Internal Audit; Human Resources; Investments; Legal and Compliance; Marketing and Communications; Sales and Relationship Management; and Technology. Whatever their background, whatever they're studying, there's a place for graduates at BlackRock.

GRADUATE VACANCIES IN 2024

FINANCE
HUMAN RESOURCES
MARKETING
SALES
TECHNOLOGY

NUMBER OF VACANCIES
100+ graduate jobs

LOCATIONS OF VACANCIES

Vacancies also available in Europe.

STARTING SALARY FOR 2024
£Competitive

WORK EXPERIENCE

| INSIGHT COURSES | DEGREE PLACEMENTS | SUMMER INTERNSHIPS |

UNIVERSITY PROMOTIONS DURING 2023-2024
Please check with your university careers service for full details of BlackRock's local promotions and events.

APPLICATION DEADLINE
Varies by function

FURTHER INFORMATION
www.Top100GraduateEmployers.com
Register now for the latest news, local promotions, work experience and graduate vacancies at BlackRock.

BlackRock

Let's invest in each other

BlackRock is a global investment manager and leading financial technology provider dedicated to helping more and more people experience financial well-being. The work we do for our clients moves markets, builds economies and supports millions of people around the globe as they save for their children's educations, home ownership or retirement.

To best serve our clients and meet their diverse needs around the world, we must bring forward an equally diverse range of perspectives and talent. It's why we're dedicated to creating an environment where our people feel welcomed, valued and supported with development opportunities, benefits and networks to help them thrive.

Explore opportunities at careers.blackrock.com/early-careers.

Stay connected @BlackRock

Bloomberg

As a global information and technology company, Bloomberg uses its dynamic network of data, ideas and analysis to solve difficult problems every day. Its customers around the world rely on them to deliver accurate, real-time business and market information that helps them make important financial decisions.

Bloomberg is guided by four core values: innovation, collaboration, customer service, and doing the right thing. The European Headquarters in London is a testament to that innovation, as it is the world's most sustainable office building.

Bloomberg offers insight weeks, internship and full-time entry-level roles at their London office across a range of business areas including Analytics & Sales, Data, Engineering, Operations and more. Candidates who join Bloomberg can build and define their own unique career, rather than a pre-defined path.

Bloomberg is proud to have a truly global dynamic organisation, so all employees are empowered to have an impact and are measured by their contributions. All graduate starters will participate in team-specific training that continues throughout their career via robust career development resources.

Bloomberg also offers internships to provide an unparalleled combination of learning, networking, and project responsibilities. The internship programme aims to provide first-hand exposure to its business and unique culture, and is filled with training, seminars, senior leader speaker series, philanthropic events, and much more.

Candidates apply online on Bloomberg's career website. The interview process will depend on the business area they have applied to, but typically involves a video and/or telephone interview followed by assessment days and in-person interviews. Bloomberg hire on a rolling basis, so early application is advised.

GRADUATE VACANCIES IN 2024
ENGINEERING
FINANCE
SALES
TECHNOLOGY

NUMBER OF VACANCIES
350 graduate jobs

LOCATIONS OF VACANCIES

STARTING SALARY FOR 2024
£Competitive
Plus competitive bonuses.

WORK EXPERIENCE
INSIGHT COURSES | DEGREE PLACEMENTS | SUMMER INTERNSHIPS

UNIVERSITY PROMOTIONS DURING 2023-2024
ASTON, BATH, BIRMINGHAM, BRISTOL, CITY UNIVERSITY LONDON, DURHAM, EDINBURGH, EXETER, IMPERIAL COLLEGE LONDON, KING'S COLLEGE LONDON, LANCASTER, LONDON SCHOOL OF ECONOMICS, MANCHESTER, NOTTINGHAM, QUEEN MARY LONDON, SCHOOL OF AFRICAN STUDIES, SOUTHAMPTON, ST ANDREWS, UNIVERSITY COLLEGE LONDON, WARWICK
Please check with your university careers service for full details of Bloomberg's local promotions and events.

MINIMUM ENTRY REQUIREMENTS
Any degree accepted

APPLICATION DEADLINE
Year-round recruitment
Early application is advised.

FURTHER INFORMATION
www.Top100GraduateEmployers.com
Register now for the latest news, local promotions, work experience and graduate vacancies at Bloomberg.

Ready to join the workplace of the future?

Our European headquarters in **London** is waiting for you.

Make it happen here.

Bloomberg

THINK BIGGER.

BRITISH AIRWAYS

 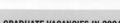

British Airways is looking to the future as an airline that loves embracing the best of modern Britain. The nation's creativity, diversity, style, wit and warmth are the same special qualities that make British Airways what it is. Now, the company is building on this spirit to make tomorrow even better.

British Airways offers several Graduate Schemes across areas including Data, Finance, Commercial, Management and Engineering. These programmes offer graduates the opportunity to complete rotational placements, working on projects that sit at the core of the business, with genuine decision-making responsibility. Graduates have the opportunity to immerse themselves in British Airways' sustainability vision, along with supporting Community Investment programmes and other important causes that are close to the company's heart.

Being a part of the British Airways graduate community gives the opportunity to engage with graduates from all schemes in the business, while also being able to learn from former graduates who are now in senior management positions. The schemes offer an excellent opportunity to explore a career in a wide variety of sectors within Aviation with hands-on practical and strategic experience. Plus, perks include access to heavily discounted flights.

Taking the first step into the world of work can be daunting, but this is a fantastic development opportunity for young people to get a well-rounded overview of the day-to-day operation of the nation's flag carrier. There is plenty of support along the way from colleagues, as well as opportunities to learn from a wide range of people across the business. The path creates new experiences and moments that allow for participants to expand their horizons.

Discover how great it feels to connect Britain with the world, and the world with Britain, with British Airways' Graduate scheme.

GRADUATE VACANCIES IN 2024

ENGINEERING

FINANCE

GENERAL MANAGEMENT

LOGISTICS

TECHNOLOGY

NUMBER OF VACANCIES
100 graduate jobs

LOCATIONS OF VACANCIES

STARTING SALARY FOR 2024
£30,000-£33,000

WORK EXPERIENCE
INSIGHT COURSES   DEGREE PLACEMENTS

UNIVERSITY PROMOTIONS DURING 2023-2024
ASTON, BIRMINGHAM, BRUNEL, CARDIFF, EDINBURGH, IMPERIAL COLLEGE LONDON, KING'S COLLEGE LONDON, LIVERPOOL, LONDON SCHOOL OF ECONOMICS, QUEEN MARY LONDON, SHEFFIELD, SOUTHAMPTON, UNIVERSITY COLLEGE LONDON, WARWICK
Please check with your university careers service for full details of British Airways' local promotions and events.

MINIMUM ENTRY REQUIREMENTS
Varies by function
Relevant degree required for some roles.

APPLICATION DEADLINE
Varies by function

FURTHER INFORMATION
www.Top100GraduateEmployers.com
Register now for the latest news, local promotions, work experience and graduate vacancies at British Airways.

THE SKY IS
NEVER THE LIMIT

EMBARK ON A CAREER PATH THAT WILL TAKE
YOU TO HEIGHTS YOU'VE NEVER IMAGINED.

Start your journey at careers.ba.com/graduates

BT Group

BT Group is the global powerhouse behind EE, BT, Plusnet, and Openreach. This international business connects friends to family, clients to colleagues, people to possibilities. It keeps the wheels of business spinning, and the emergency services responding. And it uses the power of technology to help solve big challenges, like climate change and cyber security.

From day one, graduates will have a voice at BT Group. They'll get stuck in to tough challenges, pitch in with ideas, make things happen. They won't be alone: BT Group's managers and people will be there with help and support, learning and development. Graduates will make great friends, discover new talents, and feel part of something exhilarating.

BT Group values diversity and celebrates difference. Graduates are encouraged to be themselves, whatever their background. As Philip Jansen, BT Group's CEO, says: 'We embed diversity and inclusion into everything that we do. It's fundamental to our purpose: we connect for good.' Whichever brand people are working for, everyone is playing for the same team. And they all enjoy the rewards of being part of something bigger: the opportunities to explore new experiences, pursue different dreams, and climb challenging career ladders. BT Group is always looking ahead. The company doesn't just sell broadband, and networks, and security, and thousands of clever things most people have never heard of; in its Martlesham labs, BT is inventing the technologies of the future. For graduates wanting to sharpen their skills in digital, what better place than on the cutting edge?

Four brands. One team, 100,000 strong. Together, they're connecting the world. This is an opportunity for graduates to play their part in building the BT Group of the future, one that will be net zero by 2030.

GRADUATE VACANCIES IN 2024

ENGINEERING

GENERAL MANAGEMENT

RESEARCH & DEVELOPMENT

SALES

TECHNOLOGY

NUMBER OF VACANCIES
120 graduate jobs

LOCATIONS OF VACANCIES

STARTING SALARY FOR 2024
£30,500

WORK EXPERIENCE

| DEGREE PLACEMENTS | SUMMER INTERNSHIPS |

UNIVERSITY PROMOTIONS DURING 2023-2024
ASTON, BATH, BELFAST, BIRMINGHAM, BRISTOL, CAMBRIDGE, CARDIFF, DURHAM, EDINBURGH, ESSEX, EXETER, GLASGOW, IMPERIAL COLLEGE LONDON, KING'S COLLEGE LONDON, LANCASTER, LEEDS, LEICESTER, LIVERPOOL, LOUGHBOROUGH, MANCHESTER, NEWCASTLE, NOTTINGHAM, NOTTINGHAM TRENT, OXFORD, READING, SHEFFIELD, SOUTHAMPTON, ST ANDREWS, UEA, ULSTER, UNIVERSITY COLLEGE LONDON, WARWICK, YORK

MINIMUM ENTRY REQUIREMENTS
2.2 Degree
Varies by function.
Relevant degree required for some roles.

APPLICATION DEADLINE
Year-round recruitment
Early application is advised.

FURTHER INFORMATION
www.Top100GraduateEmployers.com
*Register now for the latest news, local promotions, work experience and graduate vacancies at **BT Group**.*

BT Group

We're The Grads who connect for good

bt.com/graduates

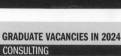

Capgemini

CapgeminiUK **f**   graduate.careers.uk@capgemini.com ✉

@CapgeminiUK **y**   linkedin.com/company/capgemini **in**

@Capgemini_UK 🔘   youtube.com/capgeminimedia ▶

Capgemini is a global leader in partnering with companies to transform and manage their business by harnessing the power of technology. The group is guided everyday by its purpose of unleashing human energy through technology for an inclusive and sustainable future.

Capgemini is a responsible and diverse organisation of 360,000 team members in more than 50 countries. With its strong 55-year heritage and deep industry expertise, Capgemini is trusted by its clients to address the entire breadth of their business needs, from strategy and design to operations, fuelled by the fast evolving and innovative world of cloud, data, AI, connectivity, software, digital engineering and platforms.

From business, consulting and client communications, to technology enthusiasts wanting to work with technology and those who have a technical background who want to build the software; a graduate at Capgemini can expect to work with the world's leading brands to enhance and transform the way they do business.

Capgemini are looking for graduates with a passion for the area they have applied for, potential, and who can demonstrate the business' seven core values including boldness, freedom, fun, trust and team spirit.

Capgemini's two-year Empower Programme focuses on giving graduates the impact skills they need for the future.

In a learning pod, graduates will explore their career aspirations, develop emotional intelligence, tackle innovation challenges from the executive team, and refine their communication skills. The programme is designed to support making a real impact on the business and create opportunities for graduates to shine.

GRADUATE VACANCIES IN 2024

CONSULTING

ENGINEERING

FINANCE

HUMAN RESOURCES

SALES

TECHNOLOGY

NUMBER OF VACANCIES
600+ graduate jobs

LOCATIONS OF VACANCIES

STARTING SALARY FOR 2024
£30,000+

WORK EXPERIENCE

| INSIGHT COURSES | DEGREE PLACEMENTS | SUMMER INTERNSHIPS |

UNIVERSITY PROMOTIONS DURING 2023-2024
ASTON, BATH, BIRMINGHAM, BRADFORD, BRISTOL, CAMBRIDGE, DURHAM, EXETER, GLASGOW, LEEDS, LEICESTER, LIVERPOOL, LOUGHBOROUGH, MANCHESTER, NEWCASTLE, NOTTINGHAM, NOTTINGHAM TRENT, OXFORD, QUEEN MARY LONDON, SHEFFIELD, SOUTHAMPTON, SURREY, SUSSEX, SWANSEA, WARWICK, YORK
Please check with your university careers service for full details of Capgemini's local promotions and events.

MINIMUM ENTRY REQUIREMENTS
Any degree accepted

APPLICATION DEADLINE
Year-round recruitment
Early application is advised.

FURTHER INFORMATION
www.Top100GraduateEmployers.com
*Register now for the latest news, local promotions, work experience and graduate vacancies at **Capgemini**.*

Capgemini

START YOUR JOURNEY

| GET THE FUTURE
| YOU WANT

capgemini.com/careers

careers.channel4.com/4skills

linkedin.com/company/channel-4 **in**

@Channel4Jobs 🐦 youtube.com/4Skills ▶

Channel 4 has been a part of its audiences' lives since 1982 and – over four decades on – it is still going strong, finding new ways to surprise, entertain, and stimulate its viewers. Today, it continues to be driven by the same purpose and a desire to be different.

Channel 4 is a publicly owned and commercially funded UK public service broadcaster with a statutory remit to deliver high-quality, innovative, alternative content that challenges the status quo.

Operating as a publisher-broadcaster, Channel 4 does not have its own in-house production teams. Instead, it commissions content from producers – mainly SMEs – from all across the nations and regions.

Channel 4 is a broadcaster with a purpose and is defined by its unique public service remit. Part of this means nurturing the talent that will help it to fulfil this remit.

Curious, hardworking graduates doing what they do best will enable Channel 4 to do what it does best: creating innovative programmes and content that reflect the UK's richly diverse cultural landscape.

Channel 4 is here to stimulate debate, to champion alternative points of view, and to inspire change in people's lives. Whoever someone is, whatever they do, they will be part of a proudly British public service broadcaster. So, for those who are just starting out in the industry or those who are wondering where they can go next, Channel 4 will happily be part of their journey.

Developing talent is a key part of Channel 4's mission. It's a duty that it not only takes seriously but embraces with open arms. Creativity, originality, inventiveness, and energy – these are the hallmarks of its output. They are the things that keeps Channel 4 fresh, and it looks for them in all of its new joiners.

GRADUATE VACANCIES IN 2024

FINANCE
GENERAL MANAGEMENT
HUMAN RESOURCES
MARKETING
MEDIA
SALES
TECHNOLOGY

NUMBER OF VACANCIES
50 graduate jobs

LOCATIONS OF VACANCIES

STARTING SALARY FOR 2024
£20,000-£30,000
Plus benefits.

WORK EXPERIENCE
INSIGHT
COURSES

UNIVERSITY PROMOTIONS DURING 2023-2024
Please check with your university careers service for full details of Channel 4's local promotions and events.

APPLICATION DEADLINE
Year-round recruitment
Early application is advised.

FURTHER INFORMATION
www.Top100GraduateEmployers.com
Register now for the latest news, local promotions, work experience and graduate vacancies at Channel 4.

Join us. Make a difference.

There is nowhere quite like Channel 4. Not in the way we entertain and stimulate our audience, nor in how we encourage and inspire the people who help us deliver for them. Publicly owned yet commercially funded, we occupy a unique place in the UK's media landscape. This is where you can start to change it, be part of it, or simply explore it.

careers.channel4.com

GRADUATE VACANCIES IN 2024

FINANCE

INVESTMENT BANKING

TECHNOLOGY

NUMBER OF VACANCIES
200+ graduate jobs

LOCATIONS OF VACANCIES

Vacancies also available in Europe, Asia, the USA and elsewhere in the world.

STARTING SALARY FOR 2024
£42,500+

WORK EXPERIENCE

| INSIGHT COURSES | DEGREE PLACEMENTS | SUMMER INTERNSHIPS |

UNIVERSITY PROMOTIONS DURING 2023-2024
Please check with your university careers service for full details of Citi's local promotions and events.

MINIMUM ENTRY REQUIREMENTS
2.1 Degree

APPLICATION DEADLINE
Varies by function

FURTHER INFORMATION
www.Top100GraduateEmployers.com
Register now for the latest news, local promotions, work experience and graduate vacancies at Citi.

Citi are in the business of banking. Through a global network of people, data and relationships they deliver financial services and leadership around the world. Working at Citi is far more than just a job. A career with them means joining a family of more than 230,000 dedicated people from around the globe.

You'll find interns and graduates throughout Citi – and they're all helping make progress. As one of the world's most global banks, Citi is committed to being the best company for early career talent. Citi offers full-time, placement and internship opportunities across a number of its business areas including Banking Capital Markets & Advisory (Investment Banking, Corporate Banking & Capital Markets), Commercial Banking, Markets, Securities Services, Treasury and Trade Solutions (TTS), Private Bank, Internal Audit, Finance Operations and Technology.

Citi also offers insight programmes enabling first year undergraduates (or 2nd year of a four year course) the opportunity to experience first-hand the Citi culture and environment.

Citi is fully committed to supporting employee growth and development from the start with extensive on-the-job training and exposure to senior leaders, as well as more traditional learning. Graduates will also have the chance to give back and make a positive impact through volunteerism.

At Citi, they believe they can use their power as a global bank to affect social change. As an employer, Citi promotes inclusive business practices and policies because it is the right thing to do. It leads to improved business performance and a better company culture where employees feel comfortable coming to work as their whole self, every day. Citi want the best talent around the world to be energized to join, motivated to stay and empowered to thrive.

for the love of
charting your own path.
for the love of progress

Civil Service
Fast Stream

GRADUATE VACANCIES IN 2024
ENGINEERING
FINANCE
GENERAL MANAGEMENT
HUMAN RESOURCES
PROPERTY
PURCHASING
RESEARCH & DEVELOPMENT
TECHNOLOGY

NUMBER OF VACANCIES
1,000 graduate jobs

LOCATIONS OF VACANCIES

STARTING SALARY FOR 2024
£28,840

WORK EXPERIENCE
SUMMER INTERNSHIPS

UNIVERSITY PROMOTIONS DURING 2023-2024
Please check with your university careers service for full details of the Civil Service's local promotions and events.

MINIMUM ENTRY REQUIREMENTS
2.2 Degree

APPLICATION DEADLINE
9th November 2023

FURTHER INFORMATION
www.Top100GraduateEmployers.com
Register now for the latest news, local promotions, work experience and graduate vacancies at the Civil Service.

The Civil Service supports the government to implement its policies on behalf of every community across the UK. The award-winning Fast Stream is the leadership and management programme that equips talented graduates from all backgrounds with the knowledge, skills and networks to operate effectively across the Civil Service.

The Fast Stream is a unique career development path. It offers proactive and ambitious graduates a choice of 15 different schemes, each one designed to help accelerate their progression to the most senior Civil Service roles. With opportunities nationwide, each scheme offers high-quality training and on-the-job learning, enabling fast streamers to build practical skills. Fast streamers gain a breadth and depth of experience, putting their knowledge into practice across a range of government department postings.

They are encouraged to take ownership of their development, pursuing a career path within a government profession. This year the Fast Stream is launching two new schemes – one focused on roles within Policy, Strategy and Government Administration, and the other on Operational Delivery. While the Fast Stream continues to offer opportunities for graduates across all degree subjects, they are keen to attract more people with STEM degrees. STEM graduates have a crucial part to play in realising the vision of building a skilled, innovative and ambitious Civil Service equipped for the future.

Fast streamers are valued members of the wider Civil Service community, where people of all ages, cultures, and backgrounds are empowered to develop their skills, knowledge and experience. They make an impact every day, helping to deliver vital public services and government operations and shaping decisions that affect everyone's lives. A range of Fast Stream networks offer a vibrant social life around work as well as enabling graduates to make lasting, professional connections.

CLYDE&CO

Clyde & Co is a global law firm providing a complete service in its core sectors of Insurance, Aviation, Healthcare, Marine, Energy & Natural Resources, Drones and Climate Change. Expanding presence in both developed and emerging markets has seen them become one of the fastest-growing law firms in the world.

Clyde & Co specialise in the sectors that move, build and power the connected world and is home to some 5,000 people across over 60 offices, including 2,400 lawyers. All of which share the same commitment to delivering exceptional client service.

At Clyde & Co, diversity fosters creativity, innovation, and better decision-making. They welcome individuals from all backgrounds, cultures, and perspectives, creating an inclusive environment where everyone can thrive. Their commitment to celebrating difference means each individual's unique voice and experiences will be valued, empowering them to make a meaningful impact and drive positive change within the firm and the legal industry.

Not looking for a specific type of person. Clyde & Co look for people who bring them something different. New ideas. New perspectives. Open-mindedness. And the kind of collaborative spirit that leads to robust solutions to complex problems.

As a graduate employer of choice, they offer exceptional training and development programs, mentorship opportunities, and a supportive culture that nurtures their growth. Join their dynamic and diverse team, where working as one, excelling with clients, celebrating difference, and acting boldly are not just words but principles they live by every day.

Take the chance to be part of a globally respected law firm that empowers graduates to thrive, make a difference, and shape the future.

GRADUATE VACANCIES IN 2024
LAW

NUMBER OF VACANCIES
75+ graduate jobs
For training contracts starting in 2026.

LOCATIONS OF VACANCIES

Vacancies also available elsewhere in the world.

STARTING SALARY FOR 2024
£20,000-£44,500

UNIVERSITY PROMOTIONS DURING 2023-2024
ASTON, BRISTOL, DURHAM, EDINBURGH, ESSEX, GLASGOW, KENT, LEICESTER, LIVERPOOL, MANCHESTER, QUEEN MARY LONDON, SCHOOL OF AFRICAN STUDIES, WARWICK
Please check with your university careers service for full details of Clyde & Co's local promotions and events.

MINIMUM ENTRY REQUIREMENTS
2.1 Degree

APPLICATION DEADLINE
Varies by function

FURTHER INFORMATION
www.Top100GraduateEmployers.com
Register now for the latest news, local promotions, work experience and graduate vacancies at Clyde & Co.

Become part of our story

If you're looking for the perfect environment to learn, develop and progress, we think you'll love life here. We're a growing law firm (one of the fastest growing in the world, in fact). We work at the heart of sectors that drive global trade and commerce. It makes this an unrivalled opportunity to take on exciting, high-profile work and to grow as rapidly as us.

law·tax·future

cmsearlytalent.com

linkedin.com/company/cms-cameron-mckenna

@cms.law.life ♪ @CMSearlytalent ⓞ youtube.com/CMS-CMCK ▶

CMS is a global law firm. They focus on the big and small. They look to the future and embrace agility and challenge. They are experts in their sectors and have the rankings to back it up. CMS embrace technology and are committed to new ideas that challenge conventional ways of doing things.

But it's not all sectors and rankings. CMS focus on relationships. They're a community. They look out for each other, encourage everyone to be themselves, and the best version of that. They're friendly and go-getting. They act with purpose and find passion in what they do.

With more than 1,100 partners and 5,000 lawyers, CMS works in cross-border teams to deliver top quality, practical advice. The firm is recognised for its sector excellence and focus in consumer products; energy; financial institutions; hotels & leisure; infrastructure & projects; life sciences & healthcare; real estate; and technology, media & telecommunications. CMS seek out different ways of thinking and doing. CMS know the best route forward is with the most diverse group of colleagues as possible. When it comes to what they're looking for, keen intellect is vital, but CMS are looking for much more than academic qualifications. Whether applicants are law students, non-law students or career changers, the skills required include personal effectiveness, professional communication, drive for achievement and having a future facing outlook.

The main route to a training contract at CMS is by successfully completing the CMS Academy programme. Their two-year training contracts feature four six-month seats or national, international, or client secondments. CMS also offers insight to the firm through their First Steps programme, apprenticeships, widening participation work experience and scholarship opportunities, and the newly launched Business Development & Marketing Graduate Programme.

GRADUATE VACANCIES IN 2024
LAW

NUMBER OF VACANCIES
95 graduate jobs
For training contracts starting in 2026

LOCATIONS OF VACANCIES

Vacancies also available elsewhere in the world.

STARTING SALARY FOR 2024
£28,000-£50,000

WORK EXPERIENCE
SUMMER
INTERNSHIPS

UNIVERSITY PROMOTIONS DURING 2023-2024
ABERDEEN, BATH, BIRMINGHAM, BRISTOL, CAMBRIDGE, CARDIFF, DUNDEE, DURHAM, EDINBURGH, EXETER, GLASGOW, LEEDS, LEICESTER, LONDON SCHOOL OF ECONOMICS, MANCHESTER, OXFORD, QUEEN MARY LONDON, SHEFFIELD, SOUTHAMPTON, STIRLING, STRATHCLYDE, WARWICK, YORK
Please check with your university careers service for full details of CMS's local promotions and events.

APPLICATION DEADLINE
December 2023

FURTHER INFORMATION
www.Top100GraduateEmployers.com
Register now for the latest news, local promotions, work experience and graduate vacancies at CMS.

Deloitte.

deloitte.co.uk/careers

DeloitteUK
@DeloitteCareers   linkedin.com/company/deloitte
@DeloitteEarlyCareers   youtube.com/DeloitteCareersUK

Deloitte makes its impact through collaboration. All around the world, their colleagues spark positive progress for their clients, people and society. Their curiousity creates all kinds of possibilities in the worlds of business and technology. There's a purpose there to believe in, and a impact that everyone can see.

By joining Deloitte, graduates will be connected to inspiring colleagues across the globe. They offer a huge range of career opportunities, where graduates can choose their own impact and build a future that suits them.

From Audit and Assurance, Tax Consulting and Legal to Technology and Consulting, Deloitte are delivering end-to-end programmes, turning complex challenges into opportunity and redesigning a more connected future.

Deloitte's incredible people challenge and inspire one another to create work with real purpose.

In every one of their twenty-one offices across the UK and offshore, successful applicants will find opportunities to work with local and global clients, connect with teams across the world and develop both their technical and personal skills.

From day one, graduates will be supported to make serious contributions to projects and the business. In a work enviroment where they are encouraged to be their true self, they can dream bigger, think creatively and deliver real impact. And, successful appplicants can grow and progress every day – learning from the work they do, and the people they collaborate with.

Across the business Deloitte's projects involve their employees working together to find the best solutions for their clients. So, throughout their time with Deloitte, graduates will connect with colleagues who share a common purpose and unite to tackle their clients' biggest challenges.

GRADUATE VACANCIES IN 2024
ACCOUNTANCY
CONSULTING
FINANCE
HUMAN RESOURCES
LAW
PROPERTY
TECHNOLOGY

NUMBER OF VACANCIES
1,500+ graduate jobs

LOCATIONS OF VACANCIES

STARTING SALARY FOR 2024
£Competitive

WORK EXPERIENCE
| INSIGHT COURSES | DEGREE PLACEMENTS | SUMMER INTERNSHIPS |

UNIVERSITY PROMOTIONS DURING 2023-2024
Please check with your university careers service for full details of Deloitte's local promotions and events.

MINIMUM ENTRY REQUIREMENTS
**2.1 Degree,
104 UCAS points**

APPLICATION DEADLINE
Varies by function

FURTHER INFORMATION
www.Top100GraduateEmployers.com
Register now for the latest news, local promotions, work experience and graduate vacancies at Deloitte.

Deloitte.

Choose Your Impact

Whichever programme you join, you'll get to know all kinds of amazing people to make positive change happen together. To inspiring colleagues in the UK and around the world. To a purpose that's shared, and that you can meaningfully contribute to. To work that challenges, and progress that never stops. To possibilities and projects in industries you may never have experienced before. And to opportunities to make a collaborative impact that reaches further and means more.

Find a career with endless opportunities to make an impact at **deloitte.co.uk/earlycareers**

Deutsche Bank is transforming the world of banking by bringing together new skills and different perspectives to innovate, progress and make a positive difference. Explore what a career in finance could look like with a variety of opportunities designed to help drive that change.

Each individual at Deutsche Bank has a part to play in reimagining banking services for corporations, governments and private individuals, worldwide. Everyone has real opportunities to drive economic growth, underpin societal progress and make a positive impact for the bank's clients, colleagues, investors and communities.

Every employee takes charge of their careers from day one. Joining a team that's truly global and connected will give an excellent foundation for an entire career. Graduates experience first-hand how the bank's inclusive and welcoming culture encourages everyone to bring their perspectives together to create innovative, tangible solutions with far-reaching impact. Ideas are heard, valued.

At Deutsche Bank, technology is the future. The innovative solutions the bank is delivering are redefining what can be achieved as a business. From updating and upgrading every system to creating own pioneering tools, the bank's technology teams are unlocking new possibilities that are being felt throughout the finance industry.

Deutsche Bank's development programme offers extensive training, exposure to stimulating projects, and the opportunity to gain the knowledge and skills needed to provide innovative products and services to their clients. For people ready to explore the true extent of their potential, Deutsche Bank is a place to gain exposure, see the bigger picture, and be inspired to challenge the status quo and drive change on a global scale.

GRADUATE VACANCIES IN 2024

FINANCE

HUMAN RESOURCES

INVESTMENT BANKING

TECHNOLOGY

NUMBER OF VACANCIES
100+ graduate jobs

LOCATIONS OF VACANCIES

Vacancies also available in Europe, Asia, the USA and elsewhere in the world.

STARTING SALARY FOR 2024
£Competitive
Plus a sign-on bonus.

WORK EXPERIENCE

| INSIGHT COURSES | DEGREE PLACEMENTS | SUMMER INTERNSHIPS |

UNIVERSITY PROMOTIONS DURING 2023-2024

ASTON, BATH, BIRMINGHAM, BRISTOL, CAMBRIDGE, CARDIFF, CITY, DURHAM, EDINBURGH, EXETER, GLASGOW, IMPERIAL COLLEGE LONDON, KING'S COLLEGE LONDON, KENT, LEEDS, LIVERPOOL, LONDON SCHOOL OF ECONOMICS, LOUGHBOROUGH, MANCHESTER, NOTTINGHAM, OXFORD, QUEEN MARY LONDON, READING, SHEFFIELD, SOUTHAMPTON, ST ANDREWS, SURREY, UNIVERSITY COLLEGE LONDON, WARWICK, YORK
Please check with your university careers service for full details of Deutsche Bank's local promotions and events.

MINIMUM ENTRY REQUIREMENTS
2.1 Degree

APPLICATION DEADLINE
Varies by function

FURTHER INFORMATION
www.Top100GraduateEmployers.com
Register now for the latest news, local promotions, work experience and graduate vacancies at Deutsche Bank.

Deutsche Bank
careers.db.com

Defining the future of finance.

Impactful work.
Feels like Deutsche Bank.

#PositiveImpact

At DLA Piper, innovation and challenging the status quo are the vital spark to how they think and what they do. Together, they create exceptional experiences, outcomes and growth for their clients and people. They make this happen with a culture where graduates bring their passion and individuality to work every day.

DLA Piper is a global business law firm with lawyers located in more than 40 countries, with over 90 offices throughout the Americas, Europe, the Middle East and Asia Pacific.

They help clients succeed through innovative and pragmatic legal solutions. Their clients range from multinational, Global 1000, and Fortune 500 enterprises, start-ups, public sector bodies and governments. DLA Piper's sector groups cover the full range of business law services.

In today's world, environmental, social and governance issues are of critical importance to business. DLA Piper are helping their clients transition to, and thrive in, a more sustainable future. They ask tough questions about purpose and transparency and find the answers together.

They are also looking for opportunities to integrate sustainability into their governance, decision-making and operations. They ensure their people have the right resources and support they need to perform and deliver at their best for clients.

DLA Piper are connected with their people, their clients and their communities in everything they do. They live by four values:

Be Supportive: They care about others, value diversity and act thoughtfully.

Be Bold: They stand tall and challenge themselves to think big.

Be Collaborative: They give, they share and they join in.

Be Exceptional: They exceed standards and expectations.

GRADUATE VACANCIES IN 2024

LAW

NUMBER OF VACANCIES
50+ graduate jobs
For training contracts starting in 2026.

LOCATIONS OF VACANCIES

Vacancies also available in Asia and elsewhere in the world.

STARTING SALARY FOR 2024
£34,000-£50,000
Paid Graduate in law conversion courses, Masters in law courses, Legal assessments exam fees (SQE) and visa costs where required.
Maintenance grants ranging £8,000-£12,000 to support Graduate and Masters studies.

WORK EXPERIENCE

INSIGHT COURSES   SUMMER INTERNSHIPS

UNIVERSITY PROMOTIONS DURING 2023-2024
ABERDEEN, BIRMINGHAM, BRISTOL, CAMBRIDGE, DURHAM, EDINBURGH, EXETER, GLASGOW, KING'S COLLEGE LONDON, LEEDS, LIVERPOOL, LONDON SCHOOL OF ECONOMICS, MANCHESTER, NEWCASTLE, NOTTINGHAM, OXFORD, SHEFFIELD, UNIVERSITY COLLEGE LONDON, WARWICK, YORK

MINIMUM ENTRY REQUIREMENTS
Any degree accepted

APPLICATION DEADLINE
1st December 2023
Early application is advised, as roles will close once DLA Piper have enough applications.

FURTHER INFORMATION
www.Top100GraduateEmployers.com
Register now for the latest news, local promotions, work experience and graduate vacancies at DLA Piper.

dyson

GRADUATE VACANCIES IN 2024

ENGINEERING

FINANCE

HUMAN RESOURCES

MARKETING

RESEARCH & DEVELOPMENT

TECHNOLOGY

NUMBER OF VACANCIES
100 graduate jobs

LOCATIONS OF VACANCIES

Dyson is growing fast. In 2012, there were 3,120 people. Today, there are over 14,000 worldwide. Dyson is focused on solving the problems that others ignore – solving them first using engineering and ingenuity. They're looking for passionate problem solvers and cutting-edge technology enthusiasts.

Dyson wants to hear from young people who strive to shake up the status quo by developing new things, different things, things that go against the grain with a diverse and global team of ingenious minds. Interns, graduates and leaders at Dyson all look to the future, thinking about the most urgent problems and finding radical and sustainable ways to solve them. This means that Dyson's scale and size grow rapidly, making it rich in new opportunities.

Dyson graduates are quick-thinking problem solvers with an insatiable curiosity. They are part of a global network – a community that supports and learns from each other. With a mission-based approach to work, they gain invaluable exposure to the inner workings of the business, through live projects with real challenges and real responsibility, getting the chance to make an impact on Dyson's future. Working alongside industry experts and senior leaders, they won't just learn how things are done, they'll find ways to make them better.

Dyson is a fulfilling place to start working life within a community of people who inspire each other. With a strong cohort of over 200 graduates in 2022 alone, there's always plenty going on outside of the office too. They're looking for people to join teams across engineering and research, marketing, finance, information technology and more. Previous graduates have worked on the future of robotics, software and digital motor technologies, as well as developing and launching the latest game-changing products, including the Dyson Zone™ headphones with air purification and the Dyson Airstrait™ straightener.

STARTING SALARY FOR 2024
£30,000

WORK EXPERIENCE

DEGREE PLACEMENTS   SUMMER INTERNSHIPS

UNIVERSITY PROMOTIONS DURING 2023-2024
BATH, BIRMINGHAM, BRISTOL, BRUNEL, EXETER, IMPERIAL COLLEGE LONDON, KING'S COLLEGE LONDON, LOUGHBOROUGH, ROYAL HOLLOWAY, SOUTHAMPTON
Please check with your university careers service for full details of Dyson's local promotions and events.

APPLICATION DEADLINE
Varies by function

FURTHER INFORMATION
www.Top100GraduateEmployers.com
*Register now for the latest news, local promotions, work experience and graduate vacancies at **Dyson**.*

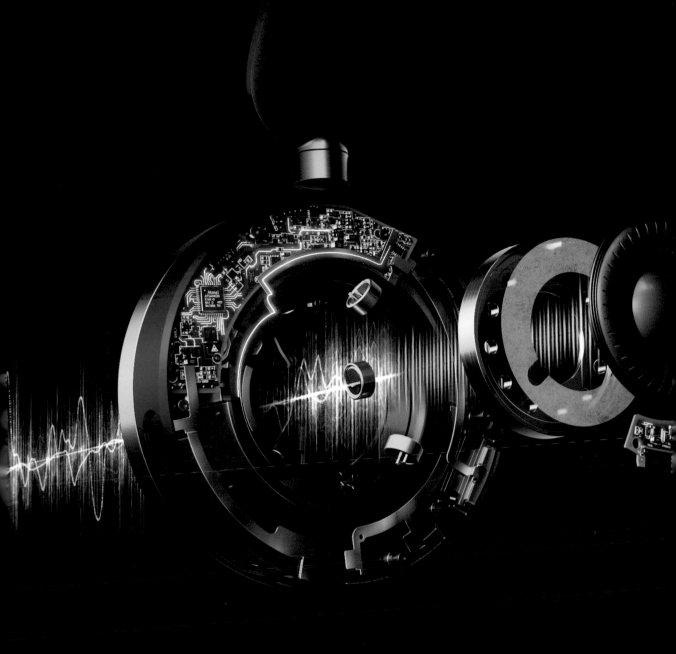

Inquisitive minds.
Disruptive technology.
Rethinkers wanted.

dyson

careers.dyson.com/early-careers

Enterprise

GRADUATE VACANCIES IN 2024
GENERAL MANAGEMENT
RETAIL
SALES

NUMBER OF VACANCIES
1,600 graduate jobs

LOCATIONS OF VACANCIES

STARTING SALARY FOR 2024
£26,100
Plus performance-based bonuses once the graduate programme has been completed, and location allowance if applicable.

WORK EXPERIENCE
DEGREE PLACEMENTS   SUMMER INTERNSHIPS

UNIVERSITY PROMOTIONS DURING 2023-2024
ABERDEEN, ABERYSTWYTH, ASTON, BANGOR, BATH, BELFAST, BIRMINGHAM, BRADFORD, BRISTOL, BRUNEL, CAMBRIDGE, CARDIFF, CITY, DUNDEE, DURHAM, EDINBURGH, ESSEX, EXETER, GLASGOW, HERIOT-WATT, HULL, IMPERIAL COLLEGE LONDON, KEELE, KING'S COLLEGE LONDON, KENT, LANCASTER, LEEDS, LEICESTER, LIVERPOOL, LONDON SCHOOL OF ECONOMICS, LOUGHBOROUGH, MANCHESTER, NEWCASTLE, NORTHUMBRIA, NOTTINGHAM, NOTTINGHAM TRENT, OXFORD, OXFORD BROOKES, PLYMOUTH, QUEEN MARY LONDON, READING, ROYAL HOLLOWAY, SCHOOL OF AFRICAN STUDIES, SHEFFIELD, SOUTHAMPTON, ST ANDREWS, STIRLING, STRATHCLYDE, SURREY, SUSSEX, SWANSEA, UEA, ULSTER, UNIVERSITY COLLEGE LONDON, WARWICK, YORK

MINIMUM ENTRY REQUIREMENTS
Any degree accepted

APPLICATION DEADLINE
Year-round recruitment

FURTHER INFORMATION
www.Top100GraduateEmployers.com
*Register now for the latest news, local promotions, work experience and graduate vacancies at **Enterprise**.*

Enterprise started life as a small business in 1957. Still family-owned, it's grown to be one of the largest global mobility providers in the world, with 10,000+ branches globally, an annual turnover of $30 billion and the biggest rental vehicle fleet on the planet.

From their senior leaders to their graduates, Enterprise gives everyone the freedom to explore their potential and the opportunities they need to rise to new challenges and take their skills to the next level – because their growth is what makes Enterprise's growth possible.

Nowhere is this philosophy better illustrated than in their approach to graduate careers. When people join their award-winning Management Training Programme, they are empowered to start contributing right from the word go. With Enterprise's dedication to training and a promote-from-within culture, their graduates gain the skills and experience needed to run their own successful multimillion-pound business in as little as two years. From there, graduates are presented with the opportunity to pursue various career paths; allowing for career progression without the need to switch companies.

As a Times Top 50 Employer for Women for 17 consecutive years, Enterprise has created a work environment where women thrive and are encouraged to advance their careers. Enterprise is also still family-owned – their CEO, Chrissy Taylor, is the third generation of the Taylor family to oversee the company's operations. This allows them to look forward even more confidently to the future, providing the stability they need to pursue the long-term good for their customers, their business, and their employees, even in these challenging times.

Join Enterprise on their Graduate Programme and become one of the new generation helping them write the next chapter of their success story.

Your future

Realise your **potential at Enterprise**

Join us on our award-winning Management Trainee programme or as an Intern and you'll enjoy great benefits, excellent training and real responsibility from day one. It starts in one of our 10,000 branches worldwide. It continues with you becoming a leader of one of those branches, in as little as two years' time. From there, you can go in whatever direction you choose. Marketing? Finance? Human resources? The choice is yours.

Get started now
careers.enterprise.co.uk

Building a better working world

ey.com/uk/students

@EY_CareersUK   EYCareersUK

linkedin.com/company/ernstandyoung

@EYUKcareers   youtube.com/EYUKCareers

As a professional services organisation, EY help companies make better decisions about business, finance and technology. The organisation has 365,000 people in more than 150 countries, working across four key business areas – Assurance, Consulting, Strategy and Transactions, and Tax.

EY transform how businesses work by using the latest technology across different sectors, helping clients find innovative solutions to their complex problems.

At EY, they empower their people with the right mindsets and skills to navigate what's next, become the transformative leaders the world needs, pursue careers as unique as they are, and build their own exceptional EY experiences. Whether they're working from home or the office, their people are encouraged to work in their own way to achieve the balance and flexibility they deserve. It's all part of adapting to the future working world. Because when everyone's story and uniqueness is celebrated, that's when we can truly transform society and build a better world for all.

As motivated and passionate members of the organisation, interns and graduates will have a personal impact – no matter which business area they join. EY provide the tools, the networks, the experiences and the opportunities for them to learn, to lead, to innovate and to grow.

Find a place and kick-start a career at EY – whether that's for two days, four weeks or three years – on one of their student programmes. EY will prepare students for the world of work and invest in their future from day one. Opportunities are available for work experience, summer internship, industrial placement and graduate programmes. This is where the adventure begins and where students have every opportunity to build an exceptional experience.

GRADUATE VACANCIES IN 2024

ACCOUNTANCY
CONSULTING
FINANCE
LAW
TECHNOLOGY

NUMBER OF VACANCIES
1,000+ graduate jobs

LOCATIONS OF VACANCIES

STARTING SALARY FOR 2024
£Competitive
Plus a comprehensive rewards and benefits package.

WORK EXPERIENCE

| INSIGHT COURSES | DEGREE PLACEMENTS | SUMMER INTERNSHIPS |

UNIVERSITY PROMOTIONS DURING 2023-2024
ABERDEEN, ASTON, BATH, BELFAST, BIRMINGHAM, BRADFORD, BRISTOL, CAMBRIDGE, CITY, DUNDEE, DURHAM, EDINBURGH, ESSEX, EXETER, GLASGOW, HERIOT-WATT, IMPERIAL COLLEGE LONDON, KING'S COLLEGE LONDON, KENT, LANCASTER, LEEDS, LEICESTER, LIVERPOOL, LONDON SCHOOL OF ECONOMICS, LOUGHBOROUGH, MANCHESTER, NEWCASTLE, NORTHUMBRIA, NOTTINGHAM, NOTTINGHAM TRENT, OXFORD, OXFORD BROOKES, PLYMOUTH, QUEEN MARY LONDON, READING, ROYAL HOLLOWAY, SCHOOL OF AFRICAN STUDIES, SHEFFIELD, SOUTHAMPTON, ST ANDREWS, STRATHCLYDE, SURREY, SUSSEX, UEA, UNIVERSITY COLLEGE LONDON, WARWICK, YORK

MINIMUM ENTRY REQUIREMENTS
Varies by function
Relevant degree required for some roles.

APPLICATION DEADLINE
Varies by function

FURTHER INFORMATION
www.Top100GraduateEmployers.com
Register now for the latest news, local promotions, work experience and graduate vacancies at EY.

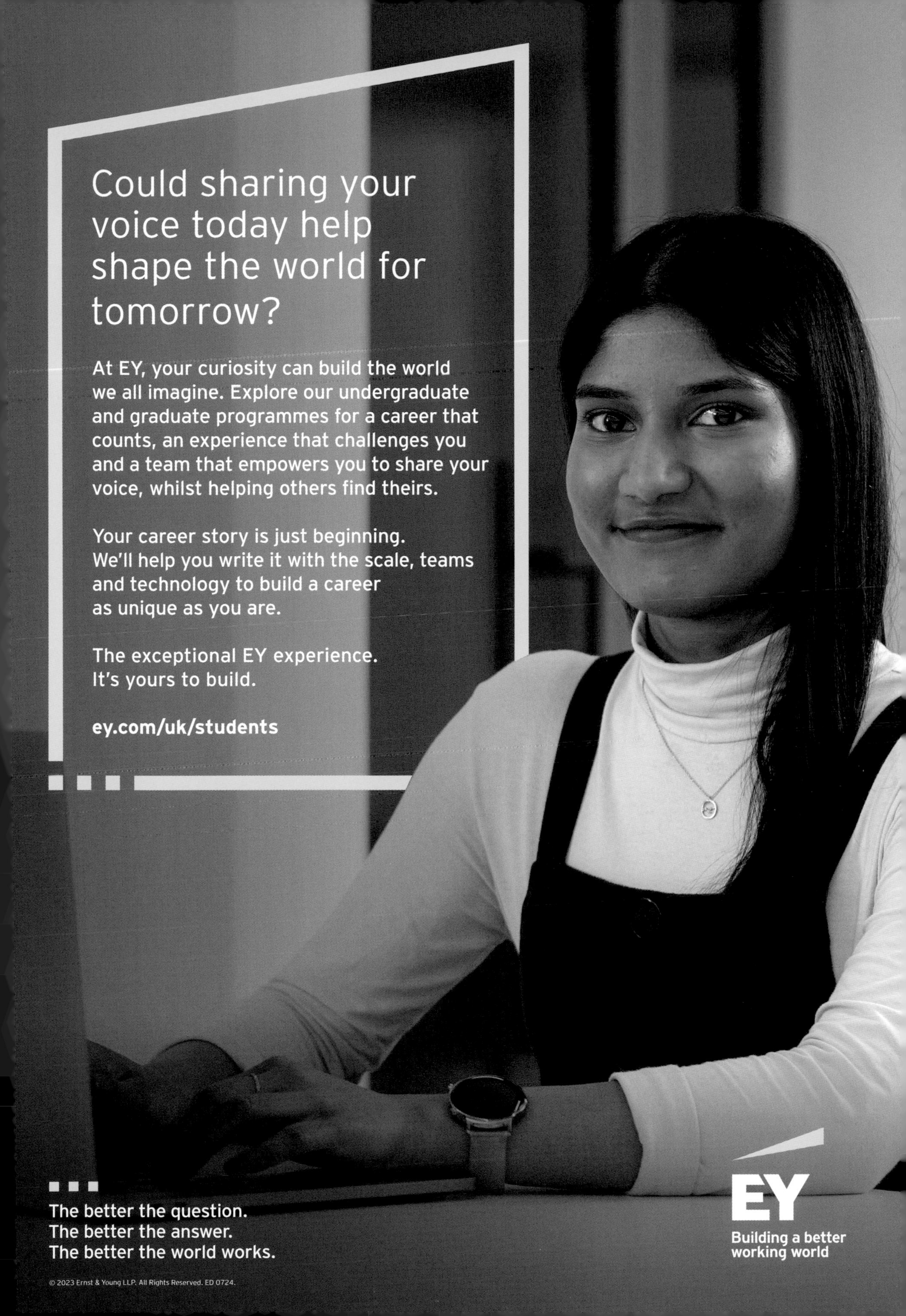

Could sharing your voice today help shape the world for tomorrow?
At EY, your curiosity can build the world we all imagine. Explore our undergraduate and graduate programmes for a career that counts, an experience that challenges you and a team that empowers you to share your voice, whilst helping others find theirs.
Your career story is just beginning. We'll help you write it with the scale, teams and technology to build a career as unique as you are.
The exceptional EY experience. It's yours to build.
ey.com/uk/students
The better the question. The better the answer. The better the world works.
EY
Building a better working world
© 2023 Ernst & Young LLP. All Rights Reserved. ED 0724.

🖋 **Freshfields**

GRADUATE VACANCIES IN 2024
LAW

NUMBER OF VACANCIES
100 graduate jobs
For training contracts starting in 2026.

LOCATIONS OF VACANCIES

Vacancies also available in Europe, the USA and Asia.

STARTING SALARY FOR 2024
£50,000
Raising to £55,000 in 2nd year of Trainee Associate Programme, and a NQ salary of £125,000.

WORK EXPERIENCE

INSIGHT COURSES | SUMMER INTERNSHIPS

UNIVERSITY PROMOTIONS DURING 2023-2024
Please check with your university careers service for full details of Freshfield's local promotions and events.

MINIMUM ENTRY REQUIREMENTS
2.1 Degree

APPLICATION DEADLINE
Varies by function

FURTHER INFORMATION
www.Top100GraduateEmployers.com
*Register now for the latest news, local promotions, work experience and graduate vacancies at **Freshfields**.*

Shape the future and make a real impact that resonates around the world. At Freshfields, exceptional opportunities await graduates who are ready to become pioneers of change. Graduates can take the first step towards an extraordinary legal career and expect more than they ever thought possible.

With Freshfields' unique eight-seat trainee associate programme, graduates have the freedom to explore and the chance to excel in diverse areas of law as they embark on an international career, filled with high-profile, precedent-setting work that transcends borders and practice areas.

Graduates can expect more than just a promising start to their career as a trainee associate. Throughout their time at Freshfields, they will receive unwavering support and guidance until they qualify and beyond.

Trainee associates at Freshfields tackle complex legal challenges for the world's leading organisations, transforming barriers into opportunities. With a presence in over 150 countries, and the opportunity for secondments abroad, trainees gain exposure to distinguished clients, complex cross-border matters and emerging fields that shape the world around us.

Freshfields takes pride in their commitment to creating a better future. Through their pro bono efforts, as well as their cutting-edge sustainability work guiding clients towards a greener future, trainees can make a real difference.

Expect a vibrant and inclusive culture at Freshfields. The firm values diversity and inclusion as cornerstones of their success, fostering an environment where everyone can thrive.

Graduates are invited to unleash their potential at Freshfields and discover a world of boundless possibilities, global reach, and the opportunity to make a lasting impact.

Expect more —

Go further with Freshfields

Learn more:
freshfields.com/ukgraduates

 **Freshfields**

Front|ine

Imagine a world where no child's life chances are limited by their social or family circumstance. That's the future Frontline is working towards. Frontline is a charity working to make life better for children with social workers, by developing excellent practice, leadership and innovation.

This is the work that 700,000 children in England rely on each year. These children need and deserve the support of life-changing social work professionals, who can keep them safe from harm, empower them to achieve their full potential and help to break the cycle of trauma and disadvantage. That's why everything Frontline does aims to make life better for these children.

This is the work where graduates will gain skills in leadership, conflict resolution, and relationship building. On the three-year Frontline programme they'll use these skills to bring about change inside the social work profession and beyond. Graduates will work directly with children and families, helping them make positive changes in their lives. Graduates will qualify as a social worker and even complete a fully-funded Master's degree.

This is the work where graduates will develop continuously. High-quality supervision and training from experienced social workers, academics, and coaches provide a rich, supportive environment for graduates to develop their professional skills and leadership. Graduates earn as they train with a bursary in year one and a salary in years two and three.

This is the work where graduates will help create social change as part of the Frontline Fellowship: a national network of social workers trained by Frontline. Graduates will receive continual support, training and funding throughout their career, to help them make a positive difference for children and families.

This is the work. This is social work.

GRADUATE VACANCIES IN 2024
SOCIAL WORK

NUMBER OF VACANCIES
500 graduate jobs

LOCATIONS OF VACANCIES

STARTING SALARY FOR 2024
£18,000-£20,000
As a tax-free bursary in year one, increasing to a £27,000+ salary from year two. Plus a fully-funded Master's degree.

WORK EXPERIENCE
SUMMER
INTERNSHIPS

UNIVERSITY PROMOTIONS DURING 2023-2024
ASTON, BIRMINGHAM, BRISTOL, BRUNEL, DURHAM, ESSEX, EXETER, HULL, KING'S COLLEGE LONDON, KENT, LANCASTER, LEEDS, LEICESTER, LIVERPOOL, MANCHESTER, NEWCASTLE, NORTHUMBRIA, NOTTINGHAM, NOTTINGHAM TRENT, OXFORD, PLYMOUTH, QUEEN MARY LONDON, SHEFFIELD, SOUTHAMPTON, SURREY, WARWICK, YORK
Please check with your university careers service for full details of Frontline's local promotions and events.

MINIMUM ENTRY REQUIREMENTS
2.2 Degree

APPLICATION DEADLINE
Year-round recruitment
Early application is advised.

FURTHER INFORMATION
www.Top100GraduateEmployers.com
Register now for the latest news, local promotions, work experience and graduate vacancies at Frontline.

Front|ine

Making social work better for children

Alex joined the Frontline programme in 2022. He currently works in an assessment and intervention team and now earns £31,000.

This is the work where you'll build the skills to help keep children safe from harm

Join our **Frontline programme** and become a children's social worker. You'll help keep children safe from harm and create positive change for them and their families.

You'll get three years of paid training and support while working in a local council social work team.

Qualify as a social worker, complete a fully-funded master's degree and learn how to work with families to protect vulnerable children.

We won't lie; it's a challenging profession. You'll help families living in the toughest circumstances and struggling with a range of pressures.

But it's also one of the most rewarding careers. The programme is designed to give you the support you'll need to thrive in the role, and the work you do will change lives for the better.

This is the work that makes a difference. This is social work.

Qualify as a social worker and complete a master's degree

Earn while you train with a tax excempt bursary in year one, and a £27,000+ salary from year two

Receive ongoing support with your career through the Fellowship

Google

Larry Page and Sergey Brin founded Google in September 1998 with a mission to organise the world's information and make it universally accessible and useful. Since then, the company has grown to more than 120,000 employees worldwide, with a wide range of popular products and platforms.

A problem isn't truly solved until it's solved for all.

Googlers build products that help create opportunities for everyone, whether down the street or across the globe. They bring insight, imagination, and a healthy disregard for the impossible. They bring everything that makes them unique. It's really the people that make Google the kind of company it is. Google hires people who are smart and determined, and favours their ability over their experience.

Google hires graduates from all disciplines, from humanities and business-related courses to engineering and computer science. The ideal candidate is someone who can demonstrate a passion for the online industry and someone who has made the most of their time at university through involvement in clubs, societies, or relevant internships. Google hires graduates who have a variety of strengths and passions, not just isolated skill sets. For technical roles within engineering teams, specific skills will be required. The diversity of perspectives, ideas, and cultures – both within Google and in the tech industry overall – leads to the creation of better products and services.

Whether it's providing online marketing consultancy, selling an advertising solution to clients, hiring the next generation of Googlers, or building products, Google has full-time roles and internships available across teams like global customer solutions, sales, people operations, legal, finance, operations, cloud, and engineering.

GRADUATE VACANCIES IN 2024
CONSULTING
ENGINEERING
HUMAN RESOURCES
MARKETING
SALES
TECHNOLOGY

NUMBER OF VACANCIES
No fixed quota

LOCATIONS OF VACANCIES

Vacancies also available in Europe.

STARTING SALARY FOR 2024
£Competitive

WORK EXPERIENCE
SUMMER INTERNSHIPS

UNIVERSITY PROMOTIONS DURING 2023-2024
Please check with your university careers service for full details of Google's local promotions and events.

MINIMUM ENTRY REQUIREMENTS
Relevant degree required for some roles.

APPLICATION DEADLINE
Year-round recruitment

FURTHER INFORMATION
www.Top100GraduateEmployers.com
Register now for the latest news, local promotions, work experience and graduate vacancies at Google.

Create
Design
Code
Build
for
everyone

At Google, we create products that make a meaningful difference for billions of users around the world. Interested in joining? Learn more about our roles, hiring process, application tips, scholarship opportunities, and more!

g.co/jobs/StudentsTimes100

◎ Grant Thornton

As one of the world's leading independent audit, tax and advisory firms, Grant Thornton is a team of independent thinkers who put quality, inclusion and integrity first. Offering a different perspective to their clients all around the world. A better experience. Delivering expertise in a way that goes beyond.

Embracing uniqueness, the culture at Grant Thornton thrives on the contributions of all the people who work there – they never settle for what is easy, and they look beyond to deliver the right thing, for everyone.

On the Grant Thornton graduate programme, there's training and support to start thriving in no time. Within three years, graduates become professionally qualified, specialising in either audit, tax or advisory.

Covering the full range of clients, experiences are truly there for the taking. And with exposure to clients from early on in their career, trainees take on real responsibility and benefit from the knowledge and experience of colleagues.

Grant Thornton's open and accessible culture gives trainees amazing opportunities to interact with senior business figures early in their career, and – with support from managers and exceptional training opportunities – the firm will do everything they can to help build the foundations for a great career.

Once qualified, the opportunities for graduates open up even further. They can keep progressing in their team, explore a different business area, or travel abroad and work at one of the 130+ Grant Thornton member firms around the world. The firm care more about an individual's potential than academic achievements alone, helping to get graduates' working lives off to a flying start. Grant Thornton is looking for people who can add value, spark fresh ideas and go beyond expectations. People that want to be able to proudly do what's right – for the firm, their colleagues, and their clients. It's how it should be.

GRADUATE VACANCIES IN 2024

ACCOUNTANCY

CONSULTING

FINANCE

NUMBER OF VACANCIES
350-400 graduate jobs

LOCATIONS OF VACANCIES

STARTING SALARY FOR 2024
£Competitive

WORK EXPERIENCE

| DEGREE PLACEMENTS | SUMMER INTERNSHIPS |

UNIVERSITY PROMOTIONS DURING 2023-2024
Please check with your university careers service for full details of Grant Thornton's local promotions and events.

MINIMUM ENTRY REQUIREMENTS
Any degree accepted

APPLICATION DEADLINE
Year-round recruitment
Early application is advised.

FURTHER INFORMATION
www.Top100GraduateEmployers.com
*Register now for the latest news, local promotions, work experience and graduate vacancies at **Grant Thornton**.*

Great minds.
Nothing alike.

If they were, we wouldn't be where we are today.
Difference of opinion is something we celebrate,
and we'll back you so you can back yourself.
Freeing up your time and energy to unlock ideas
and innovations that propel our clients, and your
career, forward. We value your potential as much
as your academic achievements. **It's how it should be.**

Audit | Tax | Advisory

Visit **trainees.grantthornton.co.uk** to learn more

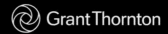

GSK

gsk.com/en-gb/careers

uk.earlytalentrecruitment@gsk.com

linkedin.com/company/glaxosmithkline **in**

GSK **f**   @GSK **y**   youtube.com/GSKvision **▶**

GSK is a global biopharma company with a special purpose – to unite science, technology and talent to get ahead of disease together. They do this by positively impacting the health of billions of people, delivering stronger, more sustainable shareholder returns as an organisation where people can thrive.

GSK's focus is to deliver a new generation of vaccines and medicines using the science of the immune system, human genetics and advanced technologies to get ahead of infectious diseases, HIV, cancer and other immune-mediated and respiratory diseases. They do all this with a commitment to operate responsibly for all their stakeholders by prioritising Innovation, Performance and Trust. Their bold ambitions for patients are reflected in new commitments to growth and a significant step-change in delivery over the next five years. This means more GSK vaccines and medicines, including innovative new products, will reach more people who need them than ever before.

GSK have long believed that building trust is key to stronger performance, helping to create value for shareholders, impact for patients and society and a reason outstanding people choose to work for and with them. That's why being a responsible business is an integral part of the GSK strategy. Taking action on environmental, social and governance issues is a key driver in their strategy.

The success of GSK absolutely depends on its people. While getting ahead of disease together is about their ambition for patients and shareholders, it's also about making GSK a place where people can thrive. GSK wants to be a place where people feel inspired, encouraged and challenged to be the best they can be. A place where they can be themselves – feel welcomed, valued and included. Where they can keep growing and look after their wellbeing.

Join GSK at this exciting moment in their journey, to get Ahead Together.

GRADUATE VACANCIES IN 2024
ENGINEERING
FINANCE
HUMAN RESOURCES
LOGISTICS
MARKETING
PURCHASING
RESEARCH & DEVELOPMENT
SALES
TECHNOLOGY

NUMBER OF VACANCIES
50+ graduate jobs

LOCATIONS OF VACANCIES

STARTING SALARY FOR 2024
£31,400
Plus an annual bonus, private healthcare and other perks.

WORK EXPERIENCE
| DEGREE PLACEMENTS | SUMMER INTERNSHIPS |

UNIVERSITY PROMOTIONS DURING 2023-2024
Please check with your university careers service for full details of GSK's local promotions and events.

APPLICATION DEADLINE
September - November 2023

FURTHER INFORMATION
www.Top100GraduateEmployers.com
Register now for the latest news, local promotions, work experience and graduate vacancies at GSK.

Ahead Together

Getting ahead of disease for 2.5 billion patients

Realise your potential on our Future Leaders Programme where you'll be empowered to take bold moves that help us impact the lives of billions of people. You'll be supported to grow, develop, and thrive. And together, we'll drive a new era of human health.

⊕ gsk.com/careers

Hogan Lovells

Defined by Difference. It's a statement of who Hogan Lovells are. It's the guiding principle that governs how they think, act, and evolve. Across their 46 offices, their 2,800+ lawyers focus on exceeding expectations. They're out there championing innovation, crossing borders, and shaping legal precedents.

How? It takes agility and ambition to stay ahead. Which is why Hogan Lovells continue to offer opportunities to students looking to get to know the firm. From vacation schemes to insight events, law fairs, webinars, workshops, and more, all their opportunities are packed with insight and practical experience.

Students will meet Hogan Lovells lawyers, delve into broad practice groups and high-profile projects, develop their own commercial awareness, and learn more about the role of a trainee solicitor. The firm's two-year training contract focuses on practical hands-on learning guided by experienced colleagues. Graduates develop a deep understanding of Hogan Lovells' bold and distinctive approach to collaborating to create valuable global solutions, as they learn from a diverse network of industry leading lawyers.

Here's how it works: graduates do four six-month seats across different practice groups – Corporate and Finance, Global Regulatory and Intellectual Property, Media and Technology, Litigation Arbitration, and Employment. Plus, for one of those seats, they'll have the chance to apply for an international or client secondment.

No matter where they come from or which path they take, Hogan Lovells provide graduates with opportunities to grow their legal acumen, sharpen their commercial edge, and tackle real challenges presented by major global clients in new and exciting ways. By supporting and encouraging them at every point in their career, they're helping them to define their own difference too.

GRADUATE VACANCIES IN 2024
LAW

NUMBER OF VACANCIES
Up to 50 graduate jobs
For training contracts starting in 2026.

LOCATIONS OF VACANCIES

STARTING SALARY FOR 2024
£50,000
Raising to £55,000 in second year.

WORK EXPERIENCE

INSIGHT COURSES | SUMMER INTERNSHIPS

UNIVERSITY PROMOTIONS DURING 2023-2024
ABERDEEN, BIRMINGHAM, BRISTOL, CAMBRIDGE, DURHAM, EXETER, KING'S COLLEGE LONDON, KENT, LEICESTER, LONDON SCHOOL OF ECONOMICS, NOTTINGHAM, OXFORD, QUEEN MARY LONDON, SCHOOL OF AFRICAN STUDIES, SURREY, UNIVERSITY COLLEGE LONDON, WARWICK
Please check with your university careers service for full details of Hogan Lovells' local promotions and events.

MINIMUM ENTRY REQUIREMENTS
2.1 Degree

APPLICATION DEADLINE
Deadline 1:
31st July 2024
Deadline 2:
31st January 2024

FURTHER INFORMATION
www.Top100GraduateEmployers.com
*Register now for the latest news, local promotions, work experience and graduate vacancies at **Hogan Lovells**.*

Join our Global community. Be a future leader.

- £50k Trainee starting salary

- 2,800+ colleagues worldwide

- 63 FTSE 100 clients

- 46 offices in 26 countries

- 54% of all our work involves three or more countries

- 150,00+ pro bono hours per year

- Over 50% of UK partners trained at the firm

- @HoganLovellsGradsUK

DEFINED BY DIFFERENCE

Hogan Lovells

With a global network across 62 countries and territories, serving more than 39 million customers, HSBC is one of the world's largest and most connected banking and financial services organisations. It is focused on opening up a world of opportunity.

HSBC is looking for students and graduates who are collaborative in action and curious thinkers – individuals with the courage to challenge the status quo and the motivation to make a positive impact for the customers they serve and the communities in which they operate.

HSBC is focused on building a sustainable future and serving the needs of a changing world. The company knows that economic growth must be sustainable for colleagues, customers, and communities. HSBC is focused on the importance of providing sustainable financial solutions to support customers in their transition to net zero – all while speeding up its own transition to becoming a net zero bank.

HSBC puts diversity at the heart of its business and provides an open, supportive, and inclusive working environment, with tailored training and support to help employees thrive on their chosen career path. No matter what interests and skills they might have, a career at HSBC will offer the opportunities, experiences, networks, and training needed – so there's no limit to how far they can go as part of an international and connected workforce.

Students and graduates can apply to join HSBC's local or global intern and graduate programmes across the bank in the following areas: Commercial Banking, Global Banking & Markets, Wealth and Personal Banking (including Global Asset Management and Private Banking), or Digital Business Services, including Operations and Technology.

GRADUATE VACANCIES IN 2024

FINANCE

GENERAL MANAGEMENT

INVESTMENT BANKING

TECHNOLOGY

NUMBER OF VACANCIES
600+ graduate jobs

LOCATIONS OF VACANCIES

Vacancies also available worldwide.

STARTING SALARY FOR 2024
£Competitve
Plus bonuses.

WORK EXPERIENCE

| INSIGHT COURSES | DEGREE PLACEMENTS | SUMMER INTERNSHIPS |

UNIVERSITY PROMOTIONS DURING 2023-2024
ABERDEEN, ABERYSTWYTH, ASTON, BANGOR, BATH, BELFAST, BIRMINGHAM, BRADFORD, BRISTOL, BRUNEL, CAMBRIDGE, CARDIFF, CITY, DUNDEE, DURHAM, EDINBURGH, ESSEX, EXETER, GLASGOW, HERIOT-WATT, HULL, IMPERIAL COLLEGE LONDON, KEELE, KING'S COLLEGE LONDON, KENT, LANCASTER, LEEDS, LEICESTER, LIVERPOOL, LONDON SCHOOL OF ECONOMICS, LOUGHBOROUGH, MANCHESTER, NEWCASTLE, NORTHUMBRIA, NOTTINGHAM, NOTTINGHAM TRENT, OXFORD, OXFORD BROOKES, PLYMOUTH, QUEEN MARY LONDON, READING, ROYAL HOLLOWAY, SCHOOL OF AFRICAN STUDIES, SHEFFIELD, SOUTHAMPTON, ST ANDREWS, STIRLING, STRATHCLYDE, SURREY, SUSSEX, SWANSEA, UEA, ULSTER, UNIVERSITY COLLEGE LONDON, WARWICK, YORK

MINIMUM ENTRY REQUIREMENTS
Varies by function
Relevant degree required for some roles.

APPLICATION DEADLINE
Varies by function

FURTHER INFORMATION
www.Top100GraduateEmployers.com
*Register now for the latest news, local promotions, work experience and graduate vacancies at **HSBC**.*

Do great minds think alike

or completely differently?

At HSBC, diversity isn't a buzzword. It's essential. That's why we encourage applications to our Global Internships and Graduate Programmes from students and graduates with any degree, from any background.

hsbc.com/earlycareers

IBM

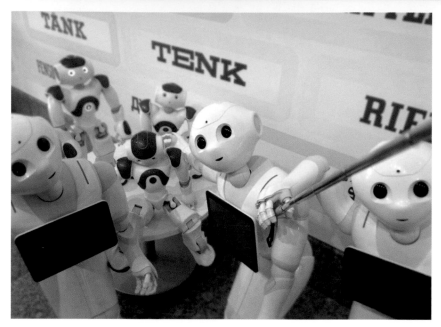

IBM is one of the world's largest technology and consulting firms. However, at IBM, work is more than a job – it's a calling: To build. To design. To code. To consult. To make markets. To invent. To collaborate. Not just to do something better, but to attempt things that people never thought possible.

IBM's graduate scheme will give graduates everything they need to build the kind of career they want. With graduate salaries starting at £32,000, a flexible benefits package and opportunities in consulting, technology and design, they will work on challenging projects, have real responsibility, and have access to world class opportunities. They'll be able to collaborate with people who are open-minded and excited about the same things they are.

IBM are looking for enthusiastic, driven and innovative individuals from any degree background. For the company's graduate schemes, applicants will have needed to achieve a 2:1 or higher in any degree discipline. IBM's most successful graduates share a distinct set of characteristics. These begin with energy and creativity, along with a clear focus on delivering exceptional customer service. IBM look for eight specific competencies during the application process: adaptability, communication, client focus, creative problem solving, teamwork, passion for IBM and taking ownership. If potential applicants love working with people and they thrive in a collaborative culture, then they'll fit right in.

Skills development is key to an IBMer's success. To further enhance their Professional Development, there are opportunities for coaching and mentoring, and these graduates will even get a dedicated manager. They will then have the opportunity to apply their knowledge in a commercial environment, via 'on-the-job training', adding value to IBM and its clients.

GRADUATE VACANCIES IN 2024

CONSULTING
TECHNOLOGY

NUMBER OF VACANCIES
150+ graduate jobs

LOCATIONS OF VACANCIES

STARTING SALARY FOR 2024
£32,000

UNIVERSITY PROMOTIONS DURING 2023-2024
ABERYSTWYTH, ASTON, BATH, BIRMINGHAM, BRADFORD, BRISTOL, BRUNEL, CARDIFF, DURHAM, EXETER, IMPERIAL COLLEGE LONDON, KING'S COLLEGE LONDON, LEEDS, LEICESTER, LIVERPOOL, LOUGHBOROUGH, MANCHESTER, NOTTINGHAM, NOTTINGHAM TRENT, OXFORD, OXFORD BROOKES, READING, SOUTHAMPTON, SURREY, UNIVERSITY COLLEGE LONDON, WARWICK
Please check with your university careers service for full details of IBM's local promotions and events.

MINIMUM ENTRY REQUIREMENTS
2.1 Degree

APPLICATION DEADLINE
Varies by function

FURTHER INFORMATION
www.Top100GraduateEmployers.com
Register now for the latest news, local promotions, work experience and graduate vacancies at IBM.

Curiosity.
Individuality.
Possibility.

ibm.com/careers

J.P.Morgan

J.P. Morgan are committed to helping businesses and markets grow and develop in more than 100 countries. Over the last 200 years, they have evolved to meet the complex financial needs of some of the world's largest companies, as well as many of the smaller businesses driving industry change.

J.P. Morgan work hard to do the right thing for their clients, shareholders, and the firm every day. Joining the firm means learning from experts in a collaborative team environment where successful applicants will be supported to make an immediate impact from the start.

Whilst academic achievements are important, they're also looking for individuality and passion, as demonstrated by extra-curricular activities. J.P. Morgan invest in helping graduates fulfil their potential as they build their career at the firm. Internship and graduate positions are available firmwide, so applicants are encouraged to learn as much as possible about the different business areas and roles. They also offer pre-internship programmes, such as Early Insights, which provide insight into the finance industry and their programmes. They often hire directly from these opportunities – giving successful applicants early exposure to the firm and how they do business.

The internship and full-time programmes they hire into are: asset management, corporate analyst development, data science & machine learning, global finance & business management, human resources, investment banking, markets, quantitative research, risk, software engineer, tech connect, wealth management, wholesale payments, and corporate banking.

Working with a team committed to doing their best, earning the trust of their clients, and encouraging employees to fulfil their potential – that's what it means to be part of J.P. Morgan.

GRADUATE VACANCIES IN 2024
ACCOUNTANCY
CONSULTING
FINANCE
GENERAL MANAGEMENT
HUMAN RESOURCES
INVESTMENT BANKING
RESEARCH & DEVELOPMENT
SALES
TECHNOLOGY

NUMBER OF VACANCIES
500 graduate jobs

LOCATIONS OF VACANCIES

Vacancies also available in Europe, Asia, the USA and elsewhere in the world.

STARTING SALARY FOR 2024
£Competitive
Annual competitive bonus.

WORK EXPERIENCE
INSIGHT COURSES | DEGREE PLACEMENTS | SUMMER INTERNSHIPS

UNIVERSITY PROMOTIONS DURING 2023-2024
ABERDEEN, ASTON, BATH, BELFAST, BIRMINGHAM, BRISTOL, CAMBRIDGE, CARDIFF, DURHAM, EDINBURGH, EXETER, GLASGOW, HERIOT-WATT, IMPERIAL COLLEGE LONDON, KING'S COLLEGE LONDON, LONDON SCHOOL OF ECONOMICS, MANCHESTER, OXFORD, PLYMOUTH, QUEEN MARY LONDON, SOUTHAMPTON, ST ANDREWS, STIRLING, STRATHCLYDE, UNIVERSITY COLLEGE LONDON, WARWICK

APPLICATION DEADLINE
27th November 2023

FURTHER INFORMATION
www.Top100GraduateEmployers.com
Register now for the latest news, local promotions, work experience and graduate vacancies at J.P. Morgan.

J.P.Morgan

Find a career
that **fits you.**

We're looking for students with varying experience levels, and all degrees and backgrounds to join our diverse, global team.

As a top employer in financial services, J.P. Morgan does much more than manage money. Here, you'll have more chances to continuously innovate, learn and make a positive impact for our clients, customers and communities.

We offer internships in over 15 different business areas as well as Insight Programs to introduce you to the industry and our company.

Explore roles at
Jpmorgan.com/careers

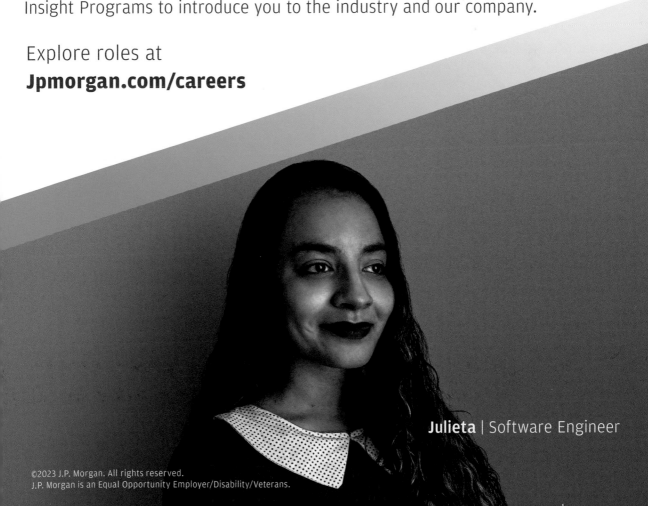

Julieta | Software Engineer

KPMG in the UK, part of a global organisation of independent firms, offers Audit, Consulting, Deal Advisory, Tax & Law and Technology services. Through the talent of over 16,000 people, the firm turns insights into opportunities, making a positive difference for businesses, people and communities.

KPMG's largest practice is Audit, which audits many of the world's largest organisations, helping to build trust in businesses and the economy. In Consulting, Deal Advisory, Tax, KPMG Law and Technology & Engineering, KPMG helps companies solve complex challenges, transforms businesses, develops confidence in markets and builds stronger communities.

Like the organisations they work with, KPMG is creating a tech-driven, sustainable business that empowers their people to connect, collaborate and deliver exceptional work. The firm is committed to creating an inclusive community where people can come as they are, work in flexible ways and thrive. The people at KPMG take care of each other and bring their unique experiences and perspectives to build a better future, together.

The firm offers a range of graduate, apprentice, insight, vacation and business placement programmes. Trainees have the chance to work with inspiring colleagues using insights, ideas and emerging technologies to deliver solutions for clients. They'll benefit from a rich learning experience, including skills development, funded professional qualifications or accreditations and mentoring, gaining learning that will last a lifetime. Through KPMG employee networks, volunteering, and community initiatives, trainees are empowered to build new friendships and make an impact outside of their day-job too.

KPMG offers challenging, yet rewarding opportunities, supports people to be their best and empowers students to build the career they want.

GRADUATE VACANCIES IN 2024

ACCOUNTANCY

CONSULTING

FINANCE

GENERAL MANAGEMENT

LAW

TECHNOLOGY

NUMBER OF VACANCIES
1,000+ graduate jobs

LOCATIONS OF VACANCIES

STARTING SALARY FOR 2024
£Competitive
Please see website for full details of KPMG's range of rewards and benefits.

WORK EXPERIENCE

DEGREE PLACEMENTS   SUMMER INTERNSHIPS

UNIVERSITY PROMOTIONS DURING 2023-2024
ABERDEEN, ASTON, BIRMINGHAM, BRISTOL, CAMBRIDGE, CARDIFF, CITY, DUNDEE, DURHAM, EDINBURGH, ESSEX, EXETER, GLASGOW, HERIOT-WATT, IMPERIAL COLLEGE LONDON, KING'S COLLEGE LONDON, LEEDS, LEICESTER, LIVERPOOL, LONDON SCHOOL OF ECONOMICS, MANCHESTER, NEWCASTLE, NORTHUMBRIA, NOTTINGHAM, NOTTINGHAM TRENT, OXFORD, PLYMOUTH, QUEEN MARY LONDON, READING, ROYAL HOLLOWAY, SHEFFIELD, SOUTHAMPTON, ST ANDREWS, STRATHCLYDE, SURREY, UEA, UNIVERSITY COLLEGE LONDON, WARWICK

APPLICATION DEADLINE
Year-round recruitment
Early application is advised.

FURTHER INFORMATION
www.Top100GraduateEmployers.com
Register now for the latest news, local promotions, work experience and graduate vacancies at KPMG.

You
bring
unique
ideas.

We make
them happen.

At KPMG, we bring people with diverse perspectives, skills and ideas together to do work that matters. Thrive in a team that will support you to succeed.

**Graduate opportunities 2024
Apply today at kpmgcareers.co.uk**

kubrick

kubrickgroup.com/uk

joinus@kubrickgroup.com ✉

linkedin.com/company/kubrick-group in

@KubrickGroup ⊙ youtube.com/KubrickGroup ▶

Kubrick was launched in 2016 to overcome the digital skills crisis by giving graduates and junior professionals the chance to enter the data and next-generation technology field through bespoke, salaried training and access to real-world client projects. Kubrick is a UK and US-based organisation.

Kubrick hires graduates and junior professionals with no technical background and train them over four months in the latest tools, technologies, and professional skills relevant to their chosen practice area.

Practices span data engineering, data management, data product, machine learning engineering, and cloud engineering, with STEM and non-STEM subjects welcome. Once trained, consultants are placed with a leading client where they apply their skills to projects over a period of two years.

Consultants receive a market-leading salary throughout training which increases throughout the two years. In addition to salaried training and real-world exposure to projects, consultants can continue developing on site through a bespoke platform and accreditations which are paid for by Kubrick.

Consultants also have access to continuous support from Kubrick throughout their training and client projects plus a wide range of benefits and can stay connected to their peers and Kubrick employers even if they choose to leave after 2 years. Kubrick has grown at a rapid rate since launching in 2016 and has since expanded into America. To date they have hired and trained over 1,800 graduates and junior professionals.

Kubrick hires diverse individuals from a wide range of backgrounds and transform them into professionals who can harness the power of data and next-generation technology, building sustainable solutions for a rapidly changing world.

GRADUATE VACANCIES IN 2024

CONSULTING
ENGINEERING
TECHNOLOGY

NUMBER OF VACANCIES
700+ graduate jobs

LOCATIONS OF VACANCIES

Vacancies also available in the USA.

STARTING SALARY FOR 2024
£33,000

UNIVERSITY PROMOTIONS DURING 2023-2024
ABERDEEN, ABERYSTWYTH, ASTON, BANGOR, BATH, BELFAST, BIRMINGHAM, BRADFORD, BRISTOL, BRUNEL, CAMBRIDGE, CARDIFF, CITY, DUNDEE, DURHAM, EDINBURGH, ESSEX, EXETER, GLASGOW, HERIOT-WATT, HULL, IMPERIAL COLLEGE LONDON, KEELE, KING'S COLLEGE LONDON, KENT, LANCASTER, LEEDS, LEICESTER, LIVERPOOL, LONDON SCHOOL OF ECONOMICS, LOUGHBOROUGH, MANCHESTER, NEWCASTLE, NORTHUMBRIA, NOTTINGHAM, NOTTINGHAM TRENT, OXFORD, OXFORD BROOKES, PLYMOUTH, QUEEN MARY LONDON, READING, ROYAL HOLLOWAY, SCHOOL OF AFRICAN STUDIES, SHEFFIELD, SOUTHAMPTON, ST ANDREWS, STIRLING, STRATHCLYDE, SURREY, SUSSEX, SWANSEA, UEA, ULSTER, UNIVERSITY COLLEGE LONDON, WARWICK, YORK

MINIMUM ENTRY REQUIREMENTS
2.1 Degree

APPLICATION DEADLINE
Please see Kubrick's website for details.

FURTHER INFORMATION
www.Top100GraduateEmployers.com
Register now for the latest news, local promotions, work experience and graduate vacancies at Kubrick.

Graduate jobs in data and next-generation technology

kubrick

Looking for a career that will open doors to unlimited opportunities, is continuously evolving, and will challenge and excite you on a daily basis? Look no further. Join our unique team and embark on an exciting journey of learning and growth. We offer a dynamic and ever-evolving environment where no day is like the other, innovation is rewarded and recognised, and collaboration is key.

- Paid to train – no experience required
- Training in the most high demand skills in Data and Next Gen tech
- Market leading remuneration
- Access to projects aligned to the skills you have learnt
- Access to leading clients across industries
- Pathway to permanent employment with client or Kubrick
- Dedicated support team
- Rapid career acceleration

Kubrick - Accelerating careers in data and next-generation technology

L'ORÉAL

L'Oréal is the world's number one beauty company, with a portfolio of 36 international brands. Their goal is to offer each and every person around the world the best of beauty in terms of quality, efficacy, safety, sincerity, and responsibility, to satisfy all beauty needs and desires in their infinite diversity.

L'Oréal UK & Ireland, the leading player in the multi-billion pound beauty industry in the UK, look for an entrepreneurial mindset in their graduates. They believe in developing their people from the ground up, providing their employees with the opportunity to grow within the company, develop a broad future focused skill set and build a dynamic career. As a result, a portion of graduate roles are filled by talents from their Internship and Spring Insights Programs, creating a future focused Early Careers journey at L'Oréal.

The remainder of the graduate roles are sourced from the external market, to ensure an equal opportunity for all candidates to join this exciting business. On the Management Trainee Program, they will work in different functions and brands across the business, gaining multiple perspectives of life at L'Oréal.

With three different rotations in their chosen stream, graduates are free to develop their strengths and discover new possibilities, shaping their future career as they go. With development programmes and their own mentor, graduates will progress into operational roles in as little as 18 months.

L'Oréal is committed to being one of the top employers in the UK, fostering a workplace where everyone feels welcomed and valued. Promoting gender equality, driving diversity and inclusion, addressing mental health, and establishing evolving workplace practices are a key focus. Through 'L'Oréal for the Future', L'Oréal's global sustainability programme, the business is driving change across all areas including product design, supply chain and consumer behaviour.

GRADUATE VACANCIES IN 2024

FINANCE
LOGISTICS
MARKETING
PURCHASING
SALES

NUMBER OF VACANCIES
25-35 graduate jobs

LOCATIONS OF VACANCIES

STARTING SALARY FOR 2024
£33,000

WORK EXPERIENCE

INSIGHT COURSES | SUMMER INTERNSHIPS

UNIVERSITY PROMOTIONS DURING 2023-2024
BATH, BIRMINGHAM, CAMBRIDGE, CARDIFF, DURHAM, EDINBURGH, EXETER, IMPERIAL COLLEGE LONDON, KING'S COLLEGE LONDON, KENT, LANCASTER, LEEDS, LIVERPOOL, LONDON SCHOOL OF ECONOMICS, LOUGHBOROUGH, MANCHESTER, NEWCASTLE, NOTTINGHAM, NOTTINGHAM TRENT, OXFORD, READING, SOUTHAMPTON, UNIVERSITY COLLEGE LONDON, WARWICK
Please check with your university careers service for full details of L'Oréal's local promotions and events.

APPLICATION DEADLINE
Varies by function

FURTHER INFORMATION
www.Top100GraduateEmployers.com
Register now for the latest news, local promotions, work experience and graduate vacancies at L'Oréal.

FREEDOM TO GO BEYOND, THAT'S THE BEAUTY OF L'ORÉAL.

L'ORÉAL

Our brands, dynamic culture, and a mindset of always being our own challenger, mean that we offer autonomy and opportunities you won't get anywhere else.

At L'Oréal UK and Ireland you are trusted to succeed.

Graduate and Internship opportunities at:
CAREERS.LOREAL.COM

LATHAM&WATKINS

lwcareers.com/london-graduate-opportunities

recruiting.graduate.lo@lw.com

Latham & Watkins is one of the world's largest law firms, with more than 3,000 lawyers in offices across Europe, the US, the Middle East, and Asia. The firm is a global leader in corporate transactions, finance matters, litigations and trials, and tax services.

Latham & Watkins' non-hierarchical, collegiate management style and ambitious and entrepreneurial culture make it a unique place to work. Over 60% of the firm's significant transactions involve four or more offices around the world, and the collaborative atmosphere is strengthened by the firm's diversity. Latham's global diversity strategy and initiatives work to strengthen and promote the firm as a workplace where the best and brightest lawyers from all walks of life excel and are supported to fulfil their potential to become firm and industry leaders. The firm offers exceptional training and support to ensure seamless collaboration on projects that span time zones, teams, and offices in the world's major financial, business, and regulatory centres.

Latham's award-winning London office is recognised for its work advising some of the world's leading corporates, financial institutions and private equity firms on market-shaping transactions, disputes, and regulatory matters.

Pro bono is a cornerstone of Latham's culture. Since 2000, Latham has provided over 4 million pro bono hours in free legal services to underserved individuals and families and the non-profit sector.

Latham provides the perfect balance of entrepreneurial spirit and career development support. It offers a training contract with real responsibility, combined with supervision from market-leading lawyers on complex, high-profile, and cross-border work. The firm looks for outstanding people who have the potential to become exceptional lawyers.

GRADUATE VACANCIES IN 2024

LAW

NUMBER OF VACANCIES
32 graduate jobs
For training contracts starting in 2026.

LOCATIONS OF VACANCIES

STARTING SALARY FOR 2024
£50,000

UNIVERSITY PROMOTIONS DURING 2023-2024
BIRMINGHAM, BRISTOL, CAMBRIDGE, CARDIFF, DURHAM, EDINBURGH, EXETER, GLASGOW, KING'S COLLEGE LONDON, KENT, LANCASTER, LEEDS, LEICESTER, LONDON SCHOOL OF ECONOMICS, MANCHESTER, NOTTINGHAM, OXFORD, QUEEN MARY LONDON, SCHOOL OF AFRICAN STUDIES, ST ANDREWS, UNIVERSITY COLLEGE LONDON, WARWICK, YORK
Please check with your university careers service for full details of Latham & Watkins' local promotions and events.

MINIMUM ENTRY REQUIREMENTS
2.1 Degree

APPLICATION DEADLINE
Varies by function

FURTHER INFORMATION
www.Top100GraduateEmployers.com
Register now for the latest news, local promotions, work experience and graduate vacancies at Latham & Watkins.

WHEN There's YOU no limit JOIN to what LATHAM you can & WATKINS achieve

It won't be long before you're working on your own transactions and cases, instead of reading up on existing ones.

At Latham & Watkins, you'll get the chance to make a big impact in small teams. And you'll be surrounded by experts who are invested in seeing you succeed.

Discover the opportunities

LATHAM & WATKINS

GRADUATE VACANCIES IN 2024
GENERAL MANAGEMENT
LOGISTICS
PURCHASING
RETAIL

NUMBER OF VACANCIES
20-30 graduate jobs

LOCATIONS OF VACANCIES

Lidl, the game-changing supermarket known for being big on quality, Lidl on price. 960+ stores. 13 warehouses. And over 31,000 colleagues nationwide. They're also big on providing the best programmes in the business, giving graduates the opportunity to really make their mark.

From being committed to sustainability, to working with local charities and food redistributors through various CSR programmes – Lidl are more than just a discount retailer. And they're looking for ambitious, dedicated talent with character and potential to join their graduate programmes. To challenge and change the world of grocery retail. And to become one of Lidl's future leaders.

Lidl's structured graduate programmes take early careers to the next level. Designed with rapid development in mind, graduates will be provided with all of the tools they need to succeed. There will be plenty of opportunity for graduates to develop, progress, and really make an impact on the business.

Lidl graduates learn from the best, with each programme uniquely tailored to provide hands on, structured training, providing a clear development path in one of Lidl's core business areas. Lidl also have Head Office graduate opportunities, based in their state-of-the-art Head Office in Tolworth, Southwest London.

From day one, graduates will build skills and realise their potential as they find out what it takes to be part of something big. A commitment to feeding the nation.

With great pay and brilliant benefits, including 30 days' holiday per year, an in-store discount, and extra discounts on gym memberships, shopping, and much more, there's never been a better time to join Lidl GB.

STARTING SALARY FOR 2024
£38,000

UNIVERSITY PROMOTIONS DURING 2023-2024
BATH, CARDIFF, GLASGOW, GREENWICH, LIVERPOOL, NORTHUMBRIA, PORTSMOUTH, SOUTHAMPTON, SURREY, WOLVERHAMPTON
Please check with your university careers service for full details of Lidl's local promotions and events.

MINIMUM ENTRY REQUIREMENTS
2.2 Degree

APPLICATION DEADLINE
Varies by function

FURTHER INFORMATION
www.Top100GraduateEmployers.com
Register now for the latest news, local promotions, work experience and graduate vacancies at Lidl.

Lidl grads.
Big characters.

**Big ambitions?
Big ideas? Big goals?
We have the graduate
programme for you.**

Save the date!

**Head Office Buying programme
launching Oct 2023**

**Nationwide programmes
launching Jan 2024**

🔍 lidlgraduatecareers.co.uk

Linklaters

Linklaters provides its people with the opportunity to shape their careers. Unlike many law firms, Linklaters has consistent, market-leading global teams across the full range of practice areas within corporate law. Wherever their lawyers focus, they are involved in the most interesting and dynamic work.

With 31 offices across 21 countries, Linklaters lawyers act for the world's leading corporates, banks, funds, governments and non-profit organisations on their most complex and challenging assignments. As a truly global business, they solve unique problems and provide exceptional development opportunities.

When people join Linklaters, they find colleagues they want to work with in a truly high performance culture. Linklaters has inspiring and personable professionals who are generous with their time and always happy to help. Their success is built on working together and they look for individuals who will collaborate and innovate to deliver the smartest solutions for clients.

Linklaters recruits candidates from a range of different backgrounds and disciplines, not just law. Why? Because those candidates bring with them a set of unique skills and perspectives that can help to challenge conventional thinking and inspire different approaches to client problems.

Over two years, trainees rotate through four seats (placements) in different practice areas, with most of trainees going on international or client secondments. To develop its exceptional talent, Linklaters are committed to providing world-class training and practical experience, alongside support, mentorship and coaching.

Attend an insight event, join a diversity and access programme, participate in a Vacation Scheme or start as a Trainee Solicitor, and graduates will find Linklaters offers outstanding, career-long opportunities.

GRADUATE VACANCIES IN 2024

LAW

NUMBER OF VACANCIES
100 graduate jobs
For training contracts starting in 2026.

LOCATIONS OF VACANCIES

STARTING SALARY FOR 2024
£50,000

WORK EXPERIENCE

INSIGHT COURSES | SUMMER INTERNSHIPS

UNIVERSITY PROMOTIONS DURING 2023-2024
ABERDEEN, ASTON, BELFAST, BIRMINGHAM, BRISTOL, CAMBRIDGE, CARDIFF, CITY, DURHAM, EDINBURGH, ESSEX, EXETER, GLASGOW, IMPERIAL COLLEGE LONDON, KING'S COLLEGE LONDON, KENT, LANCASTER, LEEDS, LEICESTER, LONDON SCHOOL OF ECONOMICS, LOUGHBOROUGH, MANCHESTER, NOTTINGHAM, NOTTINGHAM TRENT, OXFORD, OXFORD BROOKES, QUEEN MARY LONDON, SCHOOL OF AFRICAN STUDIES, SHEFFIELD, SOUTHAMPTON, ST ANDREWS, SURREY, SUSSEX, SWANSEA, UEA, UNIVERSITY COLLEGE LONDON, WARWICK, YORK

MINIMUM ENTRY REQUIREMENTS
2.1 Degree

APPLICATION DEADLINE
14th December 2023

FURTHER INFORMATION
www.Top100GraduateEmployers.com
*Register now for the latest news, local promotions, work experience and graduate vacancies at **Linklaters**.*

Linklaters

Where talent
meets opportunity

Find out more at careers.linklaters.com

LLOYDS
BANKING GROUP

lloydsbankinggrouptalent.com

lloydsbankinggrouptalent@peoplescout.co.uk

LBGEarlyTalent **f** linkedin.com/company/lloyds-banking-group **in**

LBGEarlyTalent **⊙** youtube.com/LloydsBankingGroupCareers **▶**

With over 26 million customers, Lloyds Banking Group is the largest UK retail and commercial financial services provider. It offers a wide range of opportunities to make a real impact on customers, communities, and the planet, through brands like Lloyds Bank, Halifax, Bank of Scotland and Scottish Widows.

The world is constantly evolving. New knowledge and technologies are impacting how people bank every day. To meet the ever-changing needs of their customers, Lloyds Banking Group is welcoming a new digital future. They're inviting graduates with a wide range of skills and experience to explore the possibilities of this transformation with them.

The Group is looking for graduates who are excited by rewarding challenges, who want to be part of its commitment to long-term sustainability, and who are inspired by the purpose of Helping Britain Prosper. Whether it's forming relationships with clients or developing the next generation of technology, graduates will have a real impact on the journey Lloyds Banking Group is taking.

There are a variety of graduate opportunities available – from Software Engineering to Data Science, Finance to Risk, Sustainable Financial Wellbeing and more. Whichever area graduates choose, they'll get support to achieve professional qualifications as well as long-term career progression and development.

Best of all, they'll grow in a genuinely inclusive and supportive environment, where learning is central, flexible working is championed, and everyone is free to be themselves. Because Lloyds Banking Group understands people do their best work when they feel valued, respected and trusted.

Imagine what's next, for graduates and the future of financial services, at Lloyds Banking Group.

GRADUATE VACANCIES IN 2024
ACCOUNTANCY
ENGINEERING
FINANCE
HUMAN RESOURCES
INVESTMENT BANKING
TECHNOLOGY

NUMBER OF VACANCIES
100+ graduate jobs

LOCATIONS OF VACANCIES

STARTING SALARY FOR 2024
£42,000

WORK EXPERIENCE
| INSIGHT COURSES | DEGREE PLACEMENTS | SUMMER INTERNSHIPS |

UNIVERSITY PROMOTIONS DURING 2023-2024
ASTON, BATH, BIRMINGHAM, BRISTOL, CAMBRIDGE, CARDIFF, DURHAM, EDINBURGH, GLASGOW, KING'S COLLEGE LONDON, KENT, LANCASTER, LEEDS, LIVERPOOL, LONDON SCHOOL OF ECONOMICS, MANCHESTER, NEWCASTLE, NOTTINGHAM, OXFORD, QUEEN MARY LONDON, SHEFFIELD, SOUTHAMPTON, STRATHCLYDE, UNIVERSITY COLLEGE LONDON, WARWICK, YORK

MINIMUM ENTRY REQUIREMENTS
2.2 Degree

APPLICATION DEADLINE
Varies by function

FURTHER INFORMATION
www.Top100GraduateEmployers.com
Register now for the latest news, local promotions, work experience and graduate vacancies at Lloyds Banking Group.

Where your growth is supported.

Imagine the future of financial services. Imagine technology continuing to change the way people bank. Imagine how it can become greener, more sustainable. How it can Help Britain Prosper.

Our graduates don't have to wonder. As one of our graduates, Marlon's work is already making a difference to our business and its 26 million customers. As he's helping us grow, we're helping him do the same.

Marlon is improving the products our customers use as they navigate their financial journeys, all while being supported by a hands-on team. He's developing as a person, as well as a professional, every single day.

If you want a career that promises a bright future and unlimited ways to help our business, customers and communities prosper, we've got lots of opportunities for you to explore.

Head to lloydsbankinggrouptalent.com and start imagining what's next.

Imagine what's next

MARS

GRADUATE VACANCIES IN 2024

ENGINEERING

FINANCE

GENERAL MANAGEMENT

MARKETING

RESEARCH & DEVELOPMENT

SALES

NUMBER OF VACANCIES
25 graduate jobs

LOCATIONS OF VACANCIES

STARTING SALARY FOR 2024
£33,000
Plus a £2,000 signing bonus.

UNIVERSITY PROMOTIONS DURING 2023-2024
ASTON, BATH, BIRMINGHAM, CAMBRIDGE, DURHAM, EXETER, LEEDS, MANCHESTER, NOTTINGHAM, OXFORD, UNIVERSITY COLLEGE LONDON
Please check with your university careers service for full details of Mars' local promotions and events.

MINIMUM ENTRY REQUIREMENTS
2.1 Degree

APPLICATION DEADLINE
Varies by function

FURTHER INFORMATION
www.Top100GraduateEmployers.com
Register now for the latest news, local promotions, work experience and graduate vacancies at Mars.

For generations, families across the world – including the four-legged members – have loved Mars brands, products, and services. Mars is 130,000 Associates across 80 countries, working hard to create the world's most loved products, including M&M'S®, EXTRA®, PEDIGREE®, WHISKAS®, and Dolmio®.

Mars might be a global business, but it's more like a community than a corporate – it's still a private, family-owned business built up of a family of Associates. Associates at Mars are united and guided by The Five Principles – Quality, Responsibility, Mutuality, Efficiency, and Freedom; these are key to the culture and help Associates make decisions they are proud of.

The culture at Mars is relationship-driven – and it's how these relationships are built that's most important. Collaborating with others is key. Mars encourages open communication, as this builds relationships formed of trust and respect.

Mars wants to stretch and challenge Associates every day to help them reach their full potential. So, they take learning and development seriously – it makes good business sense for Mars to have people performing at the top of their game. With great line managers, mentors, coaches and peers, graduates will be supported the whole way. And they will support other Associates to learn and grow on their journey too.

At Mars, graduates are offered an unrivalled opportunity from day one. Mars wants everything they do to matter – from the smallest things to the largest – and Mars wants their work to make a positive impact on the world around them. Graduates will have endless support to develop both personally and professionally, creating a start today, to an exciting and rewarding career tomorrow.

Start your tomorrow, today, with Mars.

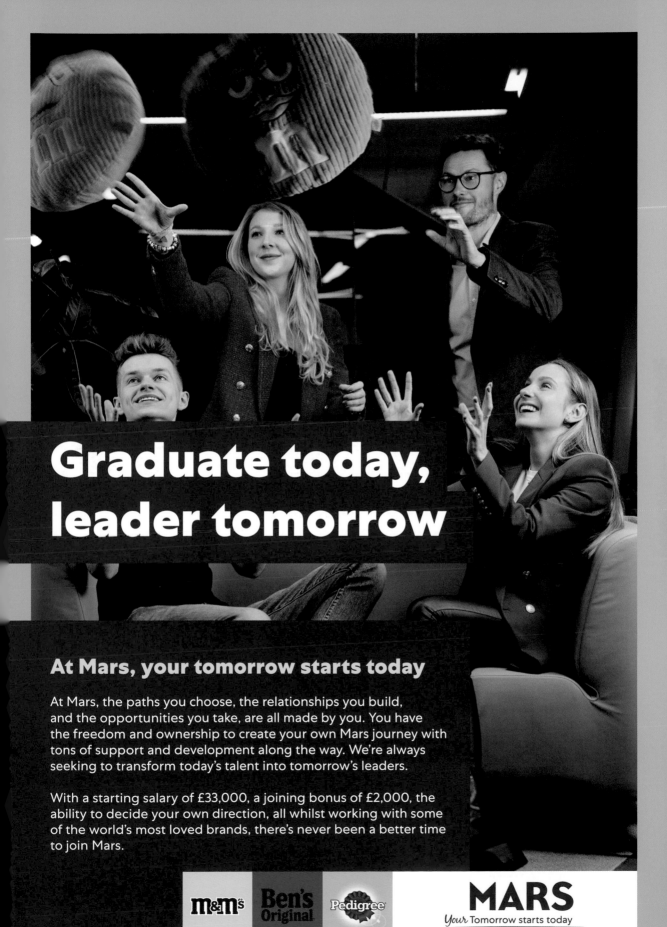

Graduate today, leader tomorrow

At Mars, your tomorrow starts today

At Mars, the paths you choose, the relationships you build, and the opportunities you take, are all made by you. You have the freedom and ownership to create your own Mars journey with tons of support and development along the way. We're always seeking to transform today's talent into tomorrow's leaders.

With a starting salary of £33,000, a joining bonus of £2,000, the ability to decide your own direction, all whilst working with some of the world's most loved brands, there's never been a better time to join Mars.

m&m's Ben's Original Pedigree

MARS
Your Tomorrow starts today

mazars

Mazars is a leading international professional services firm, who specialise in delivering exceptional quality in audit, accounting, tax, financial advisory and consulting. Mazars is present in nearly 100 countries and territories with over 47,000 professionals.

Mazars is an amazing place to learn and grow, offering individuals the chance to gain experience in a firm that truly cares about their aspirations. They pride themselves on giving their people responsibility and exposure early on in their career.

The culture is all about celebrating individuality and thrives on teamwork. Mazars gives people the freedom to make a personal contribution to their shared purpose and the team work together to deliver quality, create change, and make an impact.

Mazars is open to all disciplines and degree backgrounds and have now removed their 2.1 minimum requirement, asking instead for a strong academic record.

Mazars' services are designed around the needs of their clients, helping them to drive long-term sustainable development and growth. They invest in the expertise of their people and successful applicants will constantly develop new skills and perspectives throughout their careers.

Their opportunities include Graduate, Placement and Summer Internships throughout the year in Audit, Tax and Advisory Services. These are available nationally across 13 of their offices, meaning there is an opportunity to suit graduates in the field and location they wish to start their career.

For those who wish to explore their opportunities, check out Mazars' early careers website.

GRADUATE VACANCIES IN 2024

ACCOUNTANCY
CONSULTING
FINANCE
TECHNOLOGY

NUMBER OF VACANCIES
300-350 graduate jobs

LOCATIONS OF VACANCIES

STARTING SALARY FOR 2024
£Competitive

WORK EXPERIENCE

DEGREE PLACEMENTS   SUMMER INTERNSHIPS

UNIVERSITY PROMOTIONS DURING 2023-2024
ASTON, BATH, BIRMINGHAM, BRISTOL, CAMBRIDGE, CARDIFF, CITY, DURHAM, EDINBURGH, EXETER, GLASGOW, IMPERIAL COLLEGE LONDON, KEELE, KING'S COLLEGE LONDON, LANCASTER, LEEDS, LEICESTER, LIVERPOOL, LONDON SCHOOL OF ECONOMICS, LOUGHBOROUGH, MANCHESTER, NEWCASTLE, NORTHUMBRIA, NOTTINGHAM, NOTTINGHAM TRENT, OXFORD, PLYMOUTH, QUEEN MARY LONDON, READING, ROYAL HOLLOWAY, SHEFFIELD, SOUTHAMPTON, SURREY, SUSSEX, UNIVERSITY COLLEGE LONDON, WARWICK, YORK

MINIMUM ENTRY REQUIREMENTS
Any degree accepted

APPLICATION DEADLINE
Year-round recruitment

FURTHER INFORMATION
www.Top100GraduateEmployers.com
*Register now for the latest news, local promotions, work experience and graduate vacancies at **Mazars**.*

Mazars & me

"Finding a culture that shared my values was really important to me."

Ruth
Manager – Audit

Be yourself.
Feel part of something special.

Discover Mazars careers

MI5 helps safeguard the UK against threats to national security including terrorism and espionage. It investigates suspect individuals and organisations to gather intelligence relating to security threats. MI5 also advises the critical national infrastructure on protective security measures.

MI5 is a friendly, inclusive organisation which values diversity of background and diversity of thought. Graduates who join MI5 can expect stimulating and rewarding careers in a supportive environment, whilst enjoying a good work-life balance.

Many graduates join the Intelligence Officer Development Programme, which is a structured four-year programme designed to teach new joiners about MI5 investigations and to give them the skills to run them.

MI5 also deals with vast amounts of data, and interpreting that data is vital to its intelligence work. The Intelligence and Data Analyst Development Programme is a structured five-year programme which prepares individuals with potential to be part of this specialist career stream.

MI5 also offers a structured Technology Graduate Development Programme, which gives graduates the experience, knowledge, and skills they need to be an effective technology professional in the organisation's pioneering IT function.

Graduates who are looking for a rewarding career in corporate services can join MI5 as Business Enablers, where they can develop a breadth of experience undertaking corporate roles across a range of business areas, before having the opportunity to specialise in a particular area.

Graduates can also join as Russian or Mandarin analysts, working at the core of MI5's operational teams and using their language skills to provide intelligence insights.

GRADUATE VACANCIES IN 2024

FINANCE
GENERAL MANAGEMENT
HUMAN RESOURCES
INTELLIGENCE GATHERING
TECHNOLOGY

NUMBER OF VACANCIES
200+ graduate jobs

LOCATIONS OF VACANCIES

STARTING SALARY FOR 2024
£34,414

WORK EXPERIENCE

| INSIGHT COURSES | DEGREE PLACEMENTS | SUMMER INTERNSHIPS |

UNIVERSITY PROMOTIONS DURING 2023-2024
Please check with your university careers service for full details of MI5's local promotions and events.

MINIMUM ENTRY REQUIREMENTS
2.1 Degree
Varies by function.
Relevant degree required for some roles.

APPLICATION DEADLINE
Varies by function

FURTHER INFORMATION
www.Top100GraduateEmployers.com
Register now for the latest news, local promotions, work experience and graduate vacancies at MI5.

SHAPE
YOUR
FUTURE.

**PROTECT WHAT MATTERS
TO YOU MOST.**

JOIN THE **INTELLIGENCE
OFFICER DEVELOPMENT
PROGRAMME** AT MI5.

DISCOVER MORE AT
MI5.GOV.UK/CAREERS

 **Microsoft**

Over the last four decades, Microsoft has helped people and organisations use technology to transform how they work, live, and play. Microsoft enables digital transformation for the era of an intelligent cloud and an intelligent edge, empowering every person and every organisation to achieve more.

Alongside traditional engineering opportunities, Microsoft has Internship & Graduate roles in project management, sales, and consulting. All graduates are enrolled on a customised on-boarding process: Microsoft Aspire Experience. During a 2 year period Aspire graduates are exposed to additional trainings, tools and connections to help them thrive at Microsoft and therefore maximise their performance and learning.

Internships and Graduate positions are designed for those who thrive in dynamic environments and enjoy a challenge; who want to make an impact; and who believe that technology has the power to transform the world for better.

Whatever a new joiner's skill set, Microsoft have positions available that will challenge and develop current capabilities.

Successful candidates gain valuable experience by working on real projects that have real impact. Aspire graduates will be exposed to some of the brightest minds in the industry.

Over the course of the programme, they will work alongside other Aspire graduates and build a network of connections in over 60 countries. Microsoft do not just value difference, they seek it out and invite it in. They bring together people from across the globe and different walks of life – then support them with employee networks and employee resource groups.

Play a vital part in the business success of a high-tech global leader. Experience an inspiring world class programme. Start a Microsoft journey now.

GRADUATE VACANCIES IN 2024

CONSULTING
MARKETING
SALES
TECHNOLOGY

NUMBER OF VACANCIES
No fixed quota

LOCATIONS OF VACANCIES

STARTING SALARY FOR 2024
£Competitive
Plus benefits.

WORK EXPERIENCE
DEGREE
PLACEMENTS

UNIVERSITY PROMOTIONS DURING 2023-2024
Please check with your university careers service for full details of Microsoft's local promotions and events.

MINIMUM ENTRY REQUIREMENTS
Varies by function
Relevant degree required for some roles.

APPLICATION DEADLINE
February 2024

FURTHER INFORMATION
www.Top100GraduateEmployers.com
Register now for the latest news, local promotions, work experience and graduate vacancies at **Microsoft**.

MAKE IT. BREAK IT. MAKE IT BETTER.

When smart, creative, passionate people get together, the result can be astounding and the opportunities limitless. Microsoft are looking ahead and empowering their customers to do more and achieve more. They are obsessing about building products to solve hard challenges. They are reinventing productivity. As a graduate you will help build the future in a cloud-first, mobile-first world.

www.microsoft.co.uk/students

Morgan Stanley

Morgan Stanley is one of the world's leading financial services firms. It generates, manages and distributes capital, helping businesses get the funds they need to develop innovative products and services that benefit millions. Its work is defined by the passion and dedication of its people.

Morgan Stanley is committed to maintaining the first-class service and high standard of excellence that has always defined the firm. At its foundation are five core values – putting clients first, doing the right thing, leading with exceptional ideas, committing to diversity and inclusion, and giving back – that guides its more than 70,000 employees in 1,200 offices across 41 countries.

At Morgan Stanley, attitude is just as important as aptitude, and it seeks to work with and develop students and graduates who show integrity and commitment to the firm's core values; who share its commitment to providing first-class client service and who embrace change and innovation. Because the firm values a diversity of perspectives, it encourages people to be themselves and to pursue personal interests. This is why Morgan Stanley accepts applicants from all degree disciplines who are eager to learn and contribute.

At Morgan Stanley, goals are achieved through hiring, training and promoting the best possible talent. There are numerous opportunities to learn, grow professionally and help put the power of capital to work. Morgan Stanley programmes are designed to provide the knowledge and skills graduates can apply to develop quickly into successful professionals in their chosen area.

Training is not limited to the first weeks or months on the job but continues throughout a graduate's career. Over time, they could become part of the next generation of leaders, playing a part in technological, banking and cultural advancements that change the world forever.

GRADUATE VACANCIES IN 2024

ACCOUNTANCY
ENGINEERING
FINANCE
HUMAN RESOURCES
INVESTMENT BANKING
LAW
MARKETING
RESEARCH & DEVELOPMENT
SALES
TECHNOLOGY

NUMBER OF VACANCIES
300+ graduate jobs

LOCATIONS OF VACANCIES

STARTING SALARY FOR 2024
£Competitive
Plus benefits.

WORK EXPERIENCE

| INSIGHT COURSES | DEGREE PLACEMENTS | SUMMER INTERNSHIPS |

UNIVERSITY PROMOTIONS DURING 2023-2024
BATH, BIRMINGHAM, BRISTOL, CAMBRIDGE, CITY, DURHAM, EDINBURGH, EXETER, GLASGOW, HERIOT-WATT, IMPERIAL COLLEGE LONDON, KING'S COLLEGE LONDON, LEICESTER, LONDON SCHOOL OF ECONOMICS, LOUGHBOROUGH, MANCHESTER, NEWCASTLE, NOTTINGHAM, OXFORD, QUEEN MARY LONDON, READING, SOUTHAMPTON, ST ANDREWS, STIRLING, STRATHCLYDE, SURREY, UNIVERSITY COLLEGE LONDON, WARWICK

MINIMUM ENTRY REQUIREMENTS
2.1 Degree

APPLICATION DEADLINE
Varies by function

FURTHER INFORMATION
www.Top100GraduateEmployers.com
*Register now for the latest news, local promotions, work experience and graduate vacancies at **Morgan Stanley.***

WE ARE IN SEARCH OF GREAT MINDS THAT THINK NOTHING ALIKE.

We believe our greatest asset is our people. We value our commitment to diverse perspectives and a culture of inclusion across the firm.

A career at Morgan Stanley means belonging to an ideas-driven culture that embraces new perspectives to solve complex problems.

Discover who we are.
morganstanley.com/campus

Morgan Stanley

Mariam
Bank Resource Management

MOTT
MACDONALD

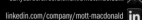

mottmac.com/careers

MottMacDonaldGroup **f** earlycareers.recruitment@mottmac.com ✉

@MottMacFuture **y** linkedin.com/company/mott-macdonald **in**

@MottMacGroup 📷 youtube.com/MottMacDonald ▶

Mott MacDonald is a global engineering, management, and development consultancy focused on guiding clients through many of the planet's most intricate challenges. By challenging norms and unlocking creativity, Mott MacDonald delivers long-lasting value for societies around the globe.

Mott MacDonald's purpose is to improve society by considering social outcomes in all they do, relentlessly focusing on excellence and digital innovation, transforming clients' businesses, their communities, and employee opportunities.

Their 16,000-strong network of experts are joined up across sectors and geographies, giving their graduates access to an exceptional breadth of expertise and experience, enhancing their knowledge with the right support and guidance every step of the way.

The consultancy's employees – active in 150 countries – take leading roles on some of the world's highest profile projects, turning obstacles into elegant, sustainable solutions. Individuals who get satisfaction from working on projects that benefit communities around the world will thrive at Mott MacDonald.

Additionally, as Mott MacDonald is an employee-owned company, it allows them to choose the work they take on and focus on the issues that are important.

Mott MacDonald's graduate schemes are more than just graduate jobs. With the help of a dedicated learning and development team, the accredited schemes aim to give graduates the opportunity to continually progress and develop in their chosen field.

All entry-level professionals are enrolled in Accelerating Your Future, a structured development programme that introduces key business and commercial competencies, enabling graduates to be the best that they can be.

GRADUATE VACANCIES IN 2024

CONSULTING

ENGINEERING

PROPERTY

TECHNOLOGY

NUMBER OF VACANCIES
500 graduate jobs

LOCATIONS OF VACANCIES

STARTING SALARY FOR 2024
£28,700-£32,500
Plus relocation allowance.

WORK EXPERIENCE

| DEGREE PLACEMENTS | SUMMER INTERNSHIPS |

UNIVERSITY PROMOTIONS DURING 2023-2024
ASTON, BATH, BIRMINGHAM, BIRMINGHAM CITY, BRISTOL, CAMBRIDGE, CARDIFF, COVENTRY, CRANFIELD, DUBLIN, DURHAM, EDINBURGH, GLASGOW, HERIOT-WATT, IMPERIAL COLLEGE LONDON, LANCASTER, LIVERPOOL, LIVERPOOL JOHN MOORS, LONDON SOUTH BANK, LOUGHBOROUGH, MANCHESTER, MANCHESTER METROPOLITAN, NEWCASTLE, NOTTINGHAM, NOTTINGHAM TRENT, READING, SHEFFIELD, SOUTHAMPTON, STRATHCLYDE, UNIVERSITY COLLEGE LONDON, ULSTER, WARWICK, WESTMINSTER

MINIMUM ENTRY REQUIREMENTS
Varies by function
Relevant degree required for some roles.

APPLICATION DEADLINE
Year-round recruitment

FURTHER INFORMATION
www.Top100GraduateEmployers.com
*Register now for the latest news, local promotions, work experience and graduate vacancies at **Mott MacDonald**.*

NatWest Group are guided by their purpose to champion potential, helping people, families and businesses to thrive. They know that when their customers and communities succeed they do too. This purpose enables them to build long term value, sustainable growth and make a positive contribution to society.

NatWest Group bring together people from varied cultures who give them broader perspectives and greater creativity. They stay hyper-focused on core values they believe everyone shares, like the need for financial security, the desire to improve a person's place in society, and the environment we all live in.

They help customers and communities improve their financial wellbeing, through initiatives like Thrive, a programme for 8-18 year olds which supports young people to develop their self-belief as well as money confidence. NatWest Group open doors to new businesses and encourage entrepreneurship particularly among underrepresented groups, and are a major funder of renewable energy projects.

They will set new joiners up to succeed, with exceptional opportunities for learning, well-being and career growth. They have insight, intern and graduate programmes across the bank so graduates can find their ideal role, no matter what their degree programme and year of study.

Teams hiring include software engineering, data & analytics, commercial banking, NatWest Markets, risk, internal audit and many more. Almost all roles are open to any degree background.

Most graduate programmes at NatWest Group are rotational allowing successful applicants to build the breadth and depth of their knowledge, and from day one they'll have a wide network of dedicated people to support them.

GRADUATE VACANCIES IN 2024
ACCOUNTANCY
FINANCE
HUMAN RESOURCES
INVESTMENT BANKING
TECHNOLOGY

NUMBER OF VACANCIES
350 graduate jobs

LOCATIONS OF VACANCIES

Vacancies also available in Europe.

STARTING SALARY FOR 2024
£33,500

WORK EXPERIENCE
INSIGHT COURSES | DEGREE PLACEMENTS | SUMMER INTERNSHIPS

UNIVERSITY PROMOTIONS DURING 2023-2024
ABERDEEN, BELFAST, BIRMINGHAM, CITY, EDINBURGH, GLASGOW, HERIOT-WATT, IMPERIAL COLLEGE LONDON, MANCHESTER, QUEEN MARY LONDON, STRATHCLYDE, WARWICK
Please check with your university careers service for full details of NatWest's local promotions and events.

MINIMUM ENTRY REQUIREMENTS
2.1 Degree

APPLICATION DEADLINE
Year-round recruitment
Early application is advised.

FURTHER INFORMATION
www.Top100GraduateEmployers.com
Register now for the latest news, local promotions, work experience and graduate vacancies at NatWest.

NatWest
Group

Welcome to the start of great

Hello! At Natwest Group we champion potential. As a graduate here, we'll help you grow a career that makes a difference.

We're a values-driven bank and that means we're inspired by a deeper purpose to help people, families and businesses of all kinds succeed and thrive.

Our customers and communities are made up of people from hugely diverse backgrounds – and so is our business. We bring together people from varied cultures who give us broader perspectives, greater creativity, and richer, deeper levels of empathy and inspiration. That's why we need you to help move our business forward.

And because you bring so much to us, we'll do everything we can to give back to you – supporting you with a rewarding work-life balance like you've never experienced before. Better still, we'll invest in your future every bit as much as you do; setting you up to succeed with exceptional opportunities for learning, well-being, and long-term career growth.

It all starts when you explore our insight, intern, and graduate programmes to find your ideal role – whatever your degree or year of study.

Open the door to your potential at **jobs.natwestgroup.com**

workatnewton.com

NewtonEurope   graduates@newtoneurope.com

@Newton_Europe linkedin.com/company/newton-europe-limited

@NewtonEurope youtube.com/@NewtonEuropeLtd

Newton is a business consultancy focused on operational improvement. An organisation that's vastly different from other players in the same industry, Newton's people are driven by a fundamental belief that even the best organisations can be better.

The difference Newton brings begins with the way they approach consulting. They work hand in hand with clients, getting to the heart of the issue. This means they are not about compiling reports; rather, it's about delivering what's in those reports. Doing the work – creating an impact. It's the best way to crack some of the largest and most complex challenges that our country faces.

Newton is filled with some of the sharpest as well as the nicest people in the industry. The enthusiasm, curiosity, tenacity and ease of communication are infectious and distinctly set the firm apart. Graduates play a big part in bringing in new perspectives, energy and potential to this thriving firm.

They are steadfast in their belief that organisations don't solve problems, people do, and this has empowered them to shape a unique culture that's all about fun, friendship and high performance.

Measurable results that significantly change the way their clients operate. For instance, working with a County Council's Children Services department, they helped reduce the number of children going into residential care from 40 per year to 17.

Newton brings together committed people who are driven to make a lasting change in an open and inclusive environment.

It inspires everyone, helps them learn and grow together and do more from day one.

GRADUATE VACANCIES IN 2024
CONSULTING

NUMBER OF VACANCIES
185 graduate jobs

LOCATIONS OF VACANCIES

STARTING SALARY FOR 2024
£45,000-£50,000
Plus a sign-on bonus of £2,500.

WORK EXPERIENCE
SUMMER INTERNSHIPS

UNIVERSITY PROMOTIONS DURING 2023-2024
BATH, BIRMINGHAM, BRISTOL, CAMBRIDGE, DURHAM, EDINBURGH, EXETER, IMPERIAL COLLEGE LONDON, LONDON SCHOOL OF ECONOMICS, MANCHESTER, NOTTINGHAM, OXFORD, STRATHCLYDE, UNIVERSITY COLLEGE LONDON, WARWICK
Please check with your university careers service for full details of Newton's local promotions and events.

MINIMUM ENTRY REQUIREMENTS
Any degree accepted

APPLICATION DEADLINE
Early 2024

FURTHER INFORMATION
www.Top100GraduateEmployers.com
Register now for the latest news, local promotions, work experience and graduate vacancies at Newton.

ACTIONS SPEAK LOUDER THAN 20,000 WORDS.

To solve our clients' challenges, we go beyond compiling reports. We implement solutions that leave a lasting impact. We work collaboratively, side-by-side, understanding their environment and the challenges they face. We analyse the data and approach the problem from different perspectives. Most importantly, we deliver results that matter. Since 2001, we've brought real and sustainable operational change to multiple industries by changing the way consulting works. At Newton, it's what we do every day. Better thinking for a better world. Let's start doing.

To find out if a career in consulting is right for you, search **Newton Graduate Careers or visit WorkatNewton.com**

Bella Somerville, Consultant

National Graduate
Development Programme

ngdp.

for Local Government

local.gov.uk/ngdp

ngdp.support@local.gov.uk

@ngdp_lga linkedin.com/company/ngdp-lga

@ngdp_localgov youtube.com/localgovassoc

The NGDP is a two-year leadership development programme for graduates to kickstart their career in local government. Graduates are placed at the heart of local communities in councils delivering over 800 different services across the country, ranging from public health, to housing, to social care.

The National Graduate Development Programme for Local Government (NGDP) is recruiting the next generation of local government leaders. It welcomes graduates motivated by a desire to lead in the public sector, who want their work to have a positive, tangible impact within communities. Graduates will have the opportunity to work flexibly within councils in locations across the country.

NGDP graduate trainees play a key role in shaping and implementing new ideas and initiatives from day one of the programme. Each trainee is employed by a local council for two years, during which time they rotate between at least three different placements across the council. NGDP trainees have pioneered digital inclusion projects, refreshed their council's corporate plans, led climate emergency initiatives, and managed town centre regeneration consultations.

Each placement allows NGDP trainees to gain valuable knowledge, experience and transferable skills, all of which make them highly sought after in the public sector workforce.

The NGDP expects to recruit a cohort of at least 250 trainees next year, placing each individual into a supportive community of peers. Councils provide placement coordinators and mentors for trainees, while the scheme's learning programme develops trainees' management and leadership skills and deepens their knowledge of the sector. Completion of the programme earns graduates a top-level Chartered Management Institute qualification.

GRADUATE VACANCIES IN 2024
GENERAL MANAGEMENT

NUMBER OF VACANCIES
250+ graduate jobs

LOCATIONS OF VACANCIES

STARTING SALARY FOR 2024
£28,000+

UNIVERSITY PROMOTIONS DURING 2023-2024
ASTON, BIRMINGHAM, BRADFORD, BRISTOL, CITY, ESSEX, IMPERIAL COLLEGE LONDON, KING'S COLLEGE LONDON, KENT, LANCASTER, LEEDS, LEICESTER, LIVERPOOL, LONDON SCHOOL OF ECONOMICS, MANCHESTER, NEWCASTLE, NORTHUMBRIA, NOTTINGHAM, NOTTINGHAM TRENT, QUEEN MARY LONDON, READING, ROYAL HOLLOWAY, SCHOOL OF AFRICAN STUDIES, SHEFFIELD, SOUTHAMPTON, SUSSEX, UEA, UNIVERSITY COLLEGE LONDON, WARWICK

MINIMUM ENTRY REQUIREMENTS
2.2 Degree

APPLICATION DEADLINE
January 2024

FURTHER INFORMATION
www.Top100GraduateEmployers.com
Register now for the latest news, local promotions, work experience and graduate vacancies at the NGDP.

Challenging. Flexible. Rewarding.
Fast track your career in local government.

Councils across the country are finding solutions to the biggest challenges facing communities, from homelessness, to social care to the climate emergency. Want to be part of it? Apply to the NGDP.

www.local.gov.uk/ngdp | @ngdp_LGA #ngdp26 | in ngdp-LGA | @ngdp_localgov

NHS

Graduate Management Training Scheme

graduates.nhs.uk

NHSGraduateScheme **f** @NHSGraduateScheme **O** @NHSGradScheme **y**

linkedin.com/company/nhs-graduate-management-training-scheme **in**

youtube.com/NHSGraduateManagementTrainingScheme **▶**

The National Health Service (NHS) is Europe's largest employer, with an annual budget of over £160 billion and a mission to improve the wellbeing of 57 million people. Its Graduate Management Training Scheme (GMTS) is a great place to begin a journey towards becoming a healthcare leader of the future.

GMTS trainees specialise in one of six areas: General Management, Human Resources, Finance, Policy & Strategy, Health Informatics or Health Analysis. Their work can be in hospital or office settings, and can range from A&E data analysis to service improvement to financial planning and much more.

Trainees get access to a comprehensive development package, including on-the-job training on placements where they gain specialist skills, and post-graduate qualifications from leading universities. On-scheme support includes pastoral and placement managers and a trainee buddy. And with 250 graduates joining GMTS in 2024 there are opportunities to build far-reaching networks with other trainees.

The Scheme has won multiple awards and gives endless ways to grow personally and professionally while taking early leadership responsibility. Graduates are selected based on their leadership potential and ambition to make a difference through a management career in healthcare.

The NHS offers both great responsibility and potential. On this fast track to senior leadership, graduates quickly face the exhilarating challenge of handling complex problems and high-profile situations. Which means future NHS leaders need the resilience, tenacity and focus to achieve the best results. Ultimately, it's an incredibly rewarding path where hard work and commitment can affect the lives of millions – and be completely life-changing for graduates themselves – in an organisation like no other in the world.

GRADUATE VACANCIES IN 2024

ACCOUNTANCY

FINANCE

GENERAL MANAGEMENT

HUMAN RESOURCES

TECHNOLOGY

NUMBER OF VACANCIES
250 graduate jobs

LOCATIONS OF VACANCIES

STARTING SALARY FOR 2024
£27,702+
Salary stated is for 2023 new starters. 2024 salary to be confirmed.

UNIVERSITY PROMOTIONS DURING 2023-2024
ASTON, BATH, BIRMINGHAM, BRADFORD, BRISTOL, BRUNEL, CAMBRIDGE, CARDIFF, CITY, DURHAM, ESSEX, EXETER, IMPERIAL COLLEGE LONDON, KING'S COLLEGE LONDON, KENT, LANCASTER, LEEDS, LEICESTER, LIVERPOOL, LOUGHBOROUGH, MANCHESTER, NEWCASTLE, NORTHUMBRIA, NOTTINGHAM, NOTTINGHAM TRENT, OXFORD, PLYMOUTH, READING, SHEFFIELD, SOUTHAMPTON, SURREY, SUSSEX, SWANSEA, UEA, UNIVERSITY COLLEGE LONDON, WARWICK, YORK
TBC. Please check with your university careers service for full details of the NHS's local promotions and events.

MINIMUM ENTRY REQUIREMENTS
2.2 Degree
Degree with numerate content required for Health Analysis roles.

APPLICATION DEADLINE
31st October 2023

FURTHER INFORMATION
www.Top100GraduateEmployers.com
Register now for the latest news, local promotions, work experience and graduate vacancies at the NHS.

NHS

Graduate Management Training Scheme

It's not who you are.
It's what you will become.

The NHS Graduate Management Training Scheme (GMTS) offers you a fast track to becoming a non-clinical senior leader. In an organisation that can positively impact 57 million people and begin a life-changing journey for you.

It's not your degree subject or the type of person you are that matters. It's your leadership potential.

Whichever GMTS specialism you join, it's about your potential to face challenges head on. To inspire and effect change.

It's about your potential to become a respected healthcare leader who helps shape the future of the NHS. And, potentially, the lives of millions.

Start your journey here

www.graduates.nhs.uk

Procter & Gamble (P&G) is one of the world's largest consumer goods companies owning iconic brands such as Gillette, Pampers, Head & Shoulders and Oral-B. With employees from over 140 countries, and operations in approximately 70 countries, P&G aspires to build a better world.

A graduate role at P&G means starting a real job with real responsibility, straight out of university. At P&G graduates won't experience any rotational programmes or gradual onboarding, instead from Day 1 they'll dive into meaningful work that makes an impact on P&G's leading brands, the world, and their career. P&G invests heavily into early career development as they promote from within their own ranks, continuously aiming to grow the skills of their employees. Whether helping to design their latest front-end innovation, selling to some of the UK's biggest retailers, or designing a full-blown product launch, P&G employees will be empowered to succeed. Most of all, P&G strives to represent the diversity of the consumers they serve, with a wide spread of nationalities represented in their UK workforce.

They want all their employees to be themselves from day one by creating a culture of acceptance and inclusion for everyone, so they can bring their unique voice to their work. P&G promotes equal voice and equal representation for everyone, and with environmental sustainability embedded into the way they do business. As a Company whose products are used every day by people all over the globe, they take their responsibility to help build a more equitable world for everyone very seriously. This is brought to life through Brand programmes such as Gillette's 'Gamechangers' – a partnership with youth education charity Football Beyond Borders to tackle racism and Fairy's #Spreadthelove campaign celebrating Pride.

GRADUATE VACANCIES IN 2024

ENGINEERING
FINANCE
HUMAN RESOURCES
LOGISTICS
MARKETING
RESEARCH & DEVELOPMENT
SALES
TECHNOLOGY

NUMBER OF VACANCIES
100 graduate jobs

LOCATIONS OF VACANCIES

Vacancies also available in Europe.

STARTING SALARY FOR 2024
£37,000+
For management graduate roles.
£27,000+ for management intern roles.

WORK EXPERIENCE

DEGREE PLACEMENTS | SUMMER INTERNSHIPS

UNIVERSITY PROMOTIONS DURING 2023-2024
ASTON, BATH, BIRMINGHAM, BRADFORD, BRISTOL, BRUNEL, CAMBRIDGE, DURHAM, EDINBURGH, GLASGOW, HERIOT-WATT, IMPERIAL COLLEGE LONDON, KINGSTON, LEEDS, LIVERPOOL, MANCHESTER, NEWCASTLE, NOTTINGHAM, QUEEN MARY LONDON, SHEFFIELD, STRATHCLYDE, UCL, WARWICK, YORK
Please check with your university careers service for full details of P&G's local promotions and events.

MINIMUM ENTRY REQUIREMENTS
Varies by function
Relevant degree required for some roles.

APPLICATION DEADLINE
Varies by function

FURTHER INFORMATION
www.Top100GraduateEmployers.com
Register now for the latest news, local promotions, work experience and graduate vacancies at P&G.

DAY 1.

Gillette

always

Make an Impact from Day 1

To learn more about careers at P&G visit **pgcareers.com**

penguinrandomhousecareers.co.uk

linkedin.com/company/penguin-random-house-uk **in**

@PenguinUKJobs 🐦 youtube.com/penguinrandomhouseuknews ▶

Penguin are the UK's largest publisher; made up of some 2,000 people and publishing over 1,500 books each year. Their doors are open to all kinds of talent. They want everyone to feel a deep sense of belonging, supported to do their best work and motivated to play a part in realising their shared purpose: to connect more people with great stories and ideas.

Collaboration, creativity, and entrepreneurship lie at the heart of what Penguin do. In a constantly evolving industry, they work hard to stretch the definition of the word publisher.

At Penguin, graduates will work with a breadth of talent from editors, technologists, designers, salespeople, publicists, digital marketers, distributors, and many others, to make each of their books a success. Together, Penguin make books for everyone, because a book can change anyone.

As one of the largest publishers in the world, Penguin offer many opportunities and all that's needed to start a successful career. Successful applicants will be supported to make decisions for themselves, and contribute to Penguin's shared mission. Penguin have amazing opportunities, great benefits, and the stability and support to be expected from a big organisation.

Graduates will develop skills through their variety of learning and development training, mentoring, and career pathways.

Each year Penguin have hundreds of entry level and early-career roles available across their creative book publishing houses and specialist support function teams.

Find out 'what's next?'. Penguin's emerging talent programmes for those at the start of their career are a great way for graduates to make their mark on a paid traineeship in one of Penguin's welcoming and supportive teams.

GRADUATE VACANCIES IN 2024
ACCOUNTANCY
FINANCE
HUMAN RESOURCES
MARKETING
MEDIA
RESEARCH & DEVELOPMENT
RETAIL
SALES
TECHNOLOGY

NUMBER OF VACANCIES
250 graduate jobs

LOCATIONS OF VACANCIES

STARTING SALARY FOR 2024
£26,500-£30,000

WORK EXPERIENCE
INSIGHT COURSES | SUMMER INTERNSHIPS

UNIVERSITY PROMOTIONS DURING 2023-2024
Please check with your university careers service for full details of Penguin's local promotions and events.

APPLICATION DEADLINE
Year-round recruitment

FURTHER INFORMATION
www.Top100GraduateEmployers.com
Register now for the latest news, local promotions, work experience and graduate vacancies at Penguin.

Your Story Starts Here

Finding a great story - editor, publisher, sales director, finance team. Making it look good - designer, copy writer, art director, illustrator. Making the finished book - production controller, product manager, quality controller. Getting it out there - marketing assistant, publicity manager, sales executive, social media manager.

Come and be part of the first of a new kind of publisher that captures the attention of the world through the stories, ideas and writing that matter.

For more than 170 years, Pfizer has worked to make a difference for all. It applies science and global resources to bring therapies to people that extend and significantly improve their lives. Every day, Pfizer colleagues work to advance wellness, prevention, treatments, and cures.

Each year, Pfizer offers up to 100 university undergraduates a 12-month industrial placement, based at one of the company's four UK sites. Whether they join in research & development, commercial, or global operations, placement students will be part of one global team, working to bring vital breakthroughs to patients. They are given a high level of responsibility as they support, manage, and deliver projects in one of the world's most innovative biopharmaceutical companies. During the programme, students will be part of a team that lets them ask questions, share ideas, make discoveries, and retain a healthy work-life balance.

Staying true to its values, Pfizer supports its new joiners to gain the courage to run with new ideas and to contribute fully to the success of the team in which they work. It provides undergraduates with a unique set of experiences that will broaden and develop the critical skill sets and competencies they will need to be successful in the business environment and to excel in their degree. Placements are listed on Pfizer's Undergraduate Vacancies webpage from September each year, with new positions added through to December.

Undergraduates who complete a successful 12-month industrial placement can apply for Pfizer UK's Future Leader Graduate Programme. But this isn't the only route available for graduates looking for a career within Pfizer. A number of entry-level roles are available across its UK sites and these opportunities are advertised throughout the year on the Pfizer Careers website.

GRADUATE VACANCIES IN 2024

ENGINEERING
FINANCE
GENERAL MANAGEMENT
LOGISTICS
MARKETING
RESEARCH & DEVELOPMENT
TECHNOLOGY

NUMBER OF VACANCIES
30-50 graduate jobs

LOCATIONS OF VACANCIES

STARTING SALARY FOR 2024
£25,000-30,000

WORK EXPERIENCE

DEGREE PLACEMENTS   SUMMER INTERNSHIPS

UNIVERSITY PROMOTIONS DURING 2023-2024
Please check with your university careers service for full details of Pfizer's local promotions and events.

MINIMUM ENTRY REQUIREMENTS
Varies by function
Relevant degree required for some roles.

APPLICATION DEADLINE
Year-round recruitment

FURTHER INFORMATION
www.Top100GraduateEmployers.com
Register now for the latest news, local promotions, work experience and graduate vacancies at Pfizer.

Pfizer

Are you ready to make breakthroughs that change patients' lives?

pfizer.co.uk/undergraduate-placements

\#FindItAtPfizer

POLICE:NOW
INFLUENCE FOR GENERATIONS

policenow.org.uk

PoliceNow   graduates@policenow.org.uk ✉

@Police_Now 🐦   linkedin.com/school/police-now in

@PoliceNowGraduates 📷   youtube.com/PoliceNowChangeTheStory ▶

With public trust at an all-time low, policing needs the right officers, right now. It's time for change. For our communities and the most vulnerable – who demand better. Police Now is a charity that transforms communities by recruiting outstanding and diverse graduates to be leaders on the policing frontline.

Police Now offers the only national graduate programmes into policing. Graduates work on big societal issues, help create safer communities and build a truly inclusive and trustworthy police service. Police Now's national programmes offer graduates a salary from day one while they train to become neighbourhood police officers or police detectives.

The training empowers graduates to make an immediate and real impact on the lives of society's most vulnerable and gain the confidence needed to drive transformative change.

Over two years, graduates expand their knowledge of the policing sector, starting with an award-winning training academy whilst being supported by a dedicated coach to aid their growth and development.

As part of the National Graduate Leadership Programme, neighbourhood police officers can apply for a four-week secondment. This is a unique opportunity to develop skills and gain valuable experience working with external partners like the Home Office. After successfully completing the two-year programme, graduates become fully warranted officers. Ongoing career and promotion support is then provided by Police Now beyond the programme and throughout their policing careers.

Graduates from all degree disciplines have the potential to become outstanding neighbourhood police officers. Few careers offer the combination to make a meaningful difference where it matters most and a lifetime of new opportunities.

GRADUATE VACANCIES IN 2024
POLICING

NUMBER OF VACANCIES
400+ graduate jobs

LOCATIONS OF VACANCIES

STARTING SALARY FOR 2024
£37,000+
London

£28,500-£31,500+
All other locations
Salary will vary depending on force. Check the website for the latest salary information.

UNIVERSITY PROMOTIONS DURING 2023-2024
ASTON, BIRMINGHAM, BIRMINGHAM CITY, BRISTOL, CARDIFF, DURHAM, EXETER, HULL, LANCASTER, LEEDS, LEICESTER, LIVERPOOL, MANCHESTER METROPOLITAN, MANCHESTER, NEWCASTLE, NOTTINGHAM TRENT, NOTTINGHAM, SHEFFIELD, UNIVERSITY OF THE WEST OF ENGLAND, WARWICK, YORK
Please check with your university careers service for full details of Police Now's local promotions and events.

MINIMUM ENTRY REQUIREMENTS
2.2 Degree

APPLICATION DEADLINE
Varies by function
Please see website for full details.

FURTHER INFORMATION
www.Top100GraduateEmployers.com
Register now for the latest news, local promotions, work experience and graduate vacancies at Police Now.

PwC are working to build trust, deliver sustained outcomes and help clients solve their most important problems by combining human ingenuity and understanding with the right technology. Join Actuarial, Audit, Business Solutions, Consulting, Deals, Legal, Operate, Risk, Tax or Technology.

PwC's global strategy, called The New Equation, brings its purpose to life by bringing its people together to strive for imaginative ways of solving their clients' most important challenges.

They're investing in the areas that matter most. Building out their capabilities in ESG and Net Zero, and combining the diverse experiences and skills of their people with innovative technology to build trust and deliver sustained outcomes.

Employing over 25,000 people across the UK, attracting, retaining and investing in the best people is critical. In some areas, this could mean working towards a professional qualification. In return they ask that joiners are eager to learn, with business awareness, intellectual and cultural curiosity and the ability to build strong relationships. They encourage their people to work together to drive impact and deliver quality to their clients.

Graduates and undergraduates can expect to be part of a stimulating environment working on challenging projects in a culture that embraces difference and empowers them to think differently. Their uniqueness and innovation is valued at PwC which is why they have 'The Deal' for all employees that ensures the experience of working there is right for everyone. Their hard work and accomplishments will be recognised and rewarded with a competitive salary and tailored, flexible benefits.

Join PwC's human-led, tech-powered team. Be a part of The New Equation.

GRADUATE VACANCIES IN 2024

ACCOUNTANCY
CONSULTING
FINANCE
LAW
TECHNOLOGY

NUMBER OF VACANCIES
1,800+ graduate jobs

LOCATIONS OF VACANCIES

STARTING SALARY FOR 2024
£Competitive

WORK EXPERIENCE

| INSIGHT | DEGREE | SUMMER |
| COURSES | PLACEMENTS | INTERNSHIPS |

UNIVERSITY PROMOTIONS DURING 2023-2024
ABERDEEN, ABERYSTWYTH, ASTON, BANGOR, BATH, BELFAST, BIRMINGHAM, BRADFORD, BRISTOL, BRUNEL, CAMBRIDGE, CARDIFF, CITY, DUNDEE, DURHAM, EDINBURGH, ESSEX, EXETER, GLASGOW, HERIOT-WATT, HULL, IMPERIAL COLLEGE LONDON, KEELE, KING'S COLLEGE LONDON, KENT, LANCASTER, LEEDS, LEICESTER, LIVERPOOL, LONDON SCHOOL OF ECONOMICS, LOUGHBOROUGH, MANCHESTER, NEWCASTLE, NORTHUMBRIA, NOTTINGHAM, NOTTINGHAM TRENT, OXFORD, OXFORD BROOKES, PLYMOUTH, QUEEN MARY LONDON, READING, ROYAL HOLLOWAY, SCHOOL OF AFRICAN STUDIES, SHEFFIELD, SOUTHAMPTON, ST ANDREWS, STIRLING, STRATHCLYDE, SURREY, SUSSEX, SWANSEA, UEA, ULSTER, UNIVERSITY COLLEGE LONDON, WARWICK, YORK

MINIMUM ENTRY REQUIREMENTS
Any degree accepted

APPLICATION DEADLINE
Varies by function

FURTHER INFORMATION
www.Top100GraduateEmployers.com
Register now for the latest news, local promotions, work experience and graduate vacancies at PwC.

Jing's story

2023 Attained qualification as a
Chartered Management Consultant

2022 Won the TechWoman100 Award and
the PwC Consulting Inclusion Award

2021 Chosen as a Digital Accelerator
and promoted to Manager

2018 Established the International
Working Group providing support
for international staff

2016 Joined PwC as a Management
Consulting Associate

Join our human-led,
tech-powered team

Jing is a Manager in our Management Consulting practice. Having originally
studied Radio and TV Journalism, she joined PwC on our Graduate
programme after completing her Masters in Intercultural Communication
at The University of Sheffield. Jing has been recognised as a TechWoman100
winner and an Inclusion and Diversity advocate at PwC. Having not come
from a technology background she's really proud of her achievements and
references her success to the support, training and guidance gained at PwC.

Be a part of The New Equation.

To find out more, visit: **pwc.co.uk/careers**

careers.rolls-royce.com

@RollsRoyce_Careers linkedin.com/company/rolls-royce

GRADUATE VACANCIES IN 2024
ENGINEERING
GENERAL MANAGEMENT
TECHNOLOGY

NUMBER OF VACANCIES
No fixed quota

LOCATIONS OF VACANCIES

STARTING SALARY FOR 2024
£28,500

WORK EXPERIENCE
DEGREE PLACEMENTS SUMMER INTERNSHIPS

UNIVERSITY PROMOTIONS DURING 2023-2024
ASTON, BATH, BIRMINGHAM, BRISTOL, CAMBRIDGE, DUNDEE, DURHAM, EDINBURGH, GLASGOW, IMPERIAL COLLEGE LONDON, LEICESTER, LOUGHBOROUGH, MANCHESTER, NOTTINGHAM, SHEFFIELD, SOUTHAMPTON, STRATHCLYDE, WARWICK
Please check with your university careers service for full details of Rolls-Royce's local promotions and events.

MINIMUM ENTRY REQUIREMENTS
2.1 Degree - 2.2 Degree
Varies by function.
Relevant degree required for some roles.

APPLICATION DEADLINE
Year-round recruitment

FURTHER INFORMATION
www.Top100GraduateEmployers.com
Register now for the latest news, local promotions, work experience and graduate vacancies at Rolls-Royce.

Rolls-Royce believes in the transforming potential of technology to protect the planet, secure the world and explore the universe. Through their complex power and propulsion solutions, this leading industrial technology company is playing an important role in helping the world transition to a low carbon economy.

Rolls-Royce believes in empowering everyone to be themselves and uncover their potential. When graduates kickstart their career with Rolls-Royce, they're defining the future on their own terms. Each journey with them starts with a strong but simple belief – everyone is unique and every Rolls-Royce journey is different.

Along with the freedom to choose the opportunities that will help them develop in the way they want, successful applicants will get the space, skills and support to discover who they can be. Because choosing their own path is what sets their achievements apart from the rest.

The world needs innovation. Rolls-Royce are focused on shaping the future of sustainable power while achieving their own net zero carbon emission targets. They're seeking candidates with a diverse range of talents and ways of thinking. People who share their vision and will challenge perceptions.

For candidates from STEM and Business with STEM disciplines, Rolls-Royce offers a wide range of graduate and internship opportunities, including entry level positions that mean candidates don't have to wait to get started in the career they want.

Learn, grow and thrive in an environment that values each employee as an individual. Graduates can explore their potential with the opportunities they choose. And be part of groundbreaking work somewhere that values everything they bring. Join Rolls-Royce.

Be You.
Be Rolls-Royce.

At Rolls-Royce, we have a long history of setting out to achieve extraordinary goals. Join us and you can help transform the way we power, protect, and connect people across the globe, secure our world, and explore the universe.

We develop and deliver complex power and propulsion solutions for safety-critical applications in the air, at sea and on land. Whether you're supporting the UK Royal Navy's nuclear submarines, enabling the transition to net zero carbon air travel, or learning what it takes to operate a leading global company, you can't innovate if you can't be yourself.

That's why we look for people with diverse talents and different ways of thinking, and give them the space, skills and support to discover their passions. All in an environment where you can be your best.

Graduate, internship and graduate direct opportunities at **careers.rolls-royce.com**

GRADUATE VACANCIES IN 2024

ENGINEERING
FINANCE
GENERAL MANAGEMENT
HUMAN RESOURCES
LAW
LOGISTICS
MEDIA
RESEARCH & DEVELOPMENT
TECHNOLOGY

NUMBER OF VACANCIES
No fixed quota

LOCATIONS OF VACANCIES

Vacancies also available elsewhere in the world.

STARTING SALARY FOR 2024
£27,000
Some roles offering a £27,000 joining bonus.

WORK EXPERIENCE

| INSIGHT COURSES | DEGREE PLACEMENTS | SUMMER INTERNSHIPS |

UNIVERSITY PROMOTIONS DURING 2023-2024
Please check with your university careers service for full details of the Royal Navy's local promotions and events.

MINIMUM ENTRY REQUIREMENTS
Relevant degree required for some roles.

APPLICATION DEADLINE
Year-round recruitment

FURTHER INFORMATION
www.Top100GraduateEmployers.com
Register now for the latest news, local promotions, work experience and graduate vacancies at the Royal Navy.

The Royal Navy is, first and foremost, a fighting force. Serving alongside Britain's allies in conflicts around the world, the Royal Navy also vitally protects UK ports, fishing grounds, and merchant ships, helping to combat international smuggling, terrorism, and piracy.

Throughout the course of history, a life at sea has always attracted those with a taste for travel and adventure; but there are plenty of other reasons for graduates and final-year students to consider a challenging and wide-ranging career with the Royal Navy.

Graduates are able to join the Royal Navy as Officers – the senior leadership and management team in the various branches, which range from engineering, sub-surface, and warfare to medical, the Fleet Air Arm, and logistics. Starting salaries of at least £27,000 – rising to approximately £33,000 in the second year – compare well with those in industry.

Those wanting to join the Royal Navy as an Engineer – with Marine, Weapon, or Air Engineer Officer, above or below the water – could work on anything from sensitive electronics to massive gas-turbine engines and nuclear weapons. Increasingly, its 30,000 personnel are involved in humanitarian and relief missions; situations where their skills, discipline, and resourcefulness make a real difference to people's lives. What's more, the Royal Navy can offer a secure, flexible career and the potential to extend to age 50.

The Royal Navy offers opportunities for early responsibility, career development, sport, recreation, and travel which exceed any in civilian life. With its global reach and responsibilities, the Royal Navy still offers plenty of adventure and the chance to see the world, while pursuing one of the most challenging, varied, and fulfilling careers available.

Santander

santander.com/en/careers/uk-careers

Aside from Santander being a bank, they're also part of one of the world's leading financial groups with 140 million customers worldwide. They've invested over 98 million euros into training and developing their people. Not only that, but they love nothing more than setting graduate potential free.

As a digital bank leading with technology, Santander has its sights on being the best open financial services platform, launching Digital Consumer Bank, intending to be the largest of its kind in the world. In response to today's demand, their engineers create cutting-edge digital services and applications for their customers across the retail and commercial banks, brought to life through access to the newest cloud-based innovative technologies.

They deliver outstanding services from exceptional people, inspired and motivated by collaboration, respect and market-leading benefits and incentives packages. It's all made possible by a culture that supports and nurtures people as they deliver their personal best every day.

Santander's Emerging Talent programmes are about bringing together talented people from a diverse range of backgrounds to make it happen. And as they embrace change, drive innovation and develop as a business, there'll be opportunities for talent to grow too.

Their graduate programme provides a solid grounding to kick-start a career. So, for those committed to making things simple, personal, and fair for customers and colleagues, bringing passion to the role, there's no better place to unleash ambition. Through these programmes graduates will have all of the support they need in order to succeed, with a dedicated graduate manager as well as continuous development – there's plenty of benefits and no shortage of opportunities to grow with Santander.

GRADUATE VACANCIES IN 2024
CONSULTING
FINANCE
SALES

NUMBER OF VACANCIES
50 graduate jobs

LOCATIONS OF VACANCIES

STARTING SALARY FOR 2024
£35,000

UNIVERSITY PROMOTIONS DURING 2023-2024
BATH, BIRMINGHAM, BRUNEL, CARDIFF, DURHAM, EDINBURGH, ESSEX, EXETER, GLASGOW, HERIOT-WATT, KING'S COLLEGE LONDON, KENT, LEEDS, LEICESTER, LONDON SCHOOL OF ECONOMICS, LOUGHBOROUGH, MANCHESTER, NEWCASTLE, NORTHUMBRIA, NOTTINGHAM, OXFORD, QUEEN MARY LONDON, SHEFFIELD, SOUTHAMPTON, SURREY, SUSSEX, SWANSEA, YORK
Please check with your university careers service for full details of Santander's local promotions and events.

MINIMUM ENTRY REQUIREMENTS
Any degree accepted

APPLICATION DEADLINE
Varies by function

FURTHER INFORMATION
www.Top100GraduateEmployers.com
Register now for the latest news, local promotions, work experience and graduate vacancies at Santander.

Graduate programmes that create happy beginnings

You have a story to write.

Your background or degree doesn't tell the whole story. We know that. That's why we're less interested in your grades, and more interested in what makes you, you. Your ideas, your perspective and your ambitions for the future.

Our graduate programmes are designed to help you lay the foundations of a page-turning career. You'll learn from the very best in the business, and get the support, training, salary and opportunities you need to go far.

The next chapter
It Starts Here

Search Santander Graduates UK to find out more

Savills is a world leading property agent, employing over 40,000 people across 700 offices. Their expertise spans the globe and they offer wide-ranging specialist knowledge. Savills take pride in providing best-in-class advice as they help individuals, businesses and institutions make better property decisions.

Savills passionately believe that their graduates are future leaders, and as such make a huge investment in them. At Savills, their best asset is their people, they are the heart of the business – which is why they are fully supported and guided to enable them to be the best versions of themselves. Savills graduates are given responsibility from day one, in teams who highly value their contribution, allowing them to be involved in some of the world's most high-profile property deals and developments. Graduates are surrounded by expert professionals and experienced team members from whom they learn and seek advice. Individual achievement is rewarded, and Savills look for graduates with entrepreneurial flair. Savills are proud to have won The Times Graduate Recruitment Award: Employer of Choice for Property for the seventeenth year running. A great work-life balance, structured training and a dynamic working environment are amongst the factors which see Savills as the preferred Property employer year-on-year.

Savills' Graduate Programme offers the chance to gain internationally recognised professional qualifications. The company offers roles within Surveying, Planning, Sustainability, Energy, Engineering, Rural, Food & Farming and Forestry, with half of these vacancies in regional locations. The company has offices in exciting locations around the UK, where Fee Earners work with varied and prestigious clients. The diversity of Savills' services means there is the flexibility to carve out a fulfilling, self-tailored career path in many locations.

GRADUATE VACANCIES IN 2024
ENGINEERING
PROPERTY

NUMBER OF VACANCIES
100+ graduate jobs

LOCATIONS OF VACANCIES

STARTING SALARY FOR 2024
£25,000-£28,000
(Subject to change)
Plus a sign-on bonus ranging £1,000-£1,500 dependent on location.

WORK EXPERIENCE
INSIGHT COURSES | DEGREE PLACEMENTS | SUMMER INTERNSHIPS

UNIVERSITY PROMOTIONS DURING 2023-2024
ABERDEEN, BANGOR, BATH, BIRMINGHAM, BRISTOL, CAMBRIDGE, CARDIFF, CITY, DURHAM, EDINBURGH, EXETER, GLASGOW, HERIOT-WATT, IMPERIAL COLLEGE LONDON, KING'S COLLEGE LONDON, LANCASTER, LEEDS, LIVERPOOL, LONDON SCHOOL OF ECONOMICS, LOUGHBOROUGH, MANCHESTER, NEWCASTLE, NORTHUMBRIA, NOTTINGHAM, NOTTINGHAM TRENT, OXFORD, OXFORD BROOKES, QUEEN MARY LONDON, READING, ROYAL HOLLOWAY, SHEFFIELD, SOUTHAMPTON, ST ANDREWS, STRATHCLYDE, SUSSEX, UNIVERSITY COLLEGE LONDON, WARWICK, YORK

MINIMUM ENTRY REQUIREMENTS
Any degree accepted

APPLICATION DEADLINE
8th November 2023

FURTHER INFORMATION
www.Top100GraduateEmployers.com
Register now for the latest news, local promotions, work experience and graduate vacancies at Savills.

SHAPE
Y**OUR** FUTURE

"I assisted with successfully pitching for the disposal of a portfolio of logistics assets across Northern Europe worth approximately €400 million"

"I have helped progress over 300 Megawatts of energy for the UK power grid through renewable developments - enough to power nearly 200,000 homes"

18 possible career paths	**2-3** year training programme with permanent employment contract	**17** Years as The Times Graduate Employer of Choice for Property
40% of our main board joined as graduate trainees	**39,000+** global employees	**600+** offices in over 70 countries

A career in real estate offers an exciting and dynamic career path with the opportunity to specialise in several different areas that help shape the future of our built environment.

Become **the future of Savills**

@ @savillsinstagrad   #careersinproperty

savills

SECRET INTELLIGENCE SERVICE MI6

sis.gov.uk/explore-careers.html

Everyone at MI6 is united by the mission of protecting the UK's security and economic wellbeing. Through the provision of secret intelligence, MI6 ensure the Government can face major challenges presented by terrorism, cyber-threats and regional instability.

MI6 offers graduates incredibly rewarding careers in a supportive environment. There are over 100 opportunities in areas such as intelligence gathering, technology and general management. Graduates will work with some of the best minds in their fields, gaining valuable insights into unique projects.

Many people apply for MI6's Intelligence Officer role. Graduates are based in London while completing their initial training, after this they could then be posted overseas, where they will have the chance to experience new cultures and run intelligence gathering operations. It's a role that relies on strong communication skills and the ability to develop trusted relationships.

Graduates with a STEM degree can join MI6's Technology Graduate Development Programme. Over two years, graduates receive extensive internal and broader external training gaining hands-on experience alongside specialist teams. Graduates work across a range of specialisms including software engineering, business analysts, UX design, data science, machine learning, information, and cyber security.

Whatever path they choose, successful applicants will play an important part in MI6's mission, and will change roles every three years. This is hugely beneficial as it helps to build up a breadth of skills, experiences, and insights.

To apply to MI6, all graduates need to be British citizens or have dual British nationality.

GRADUATE VACANCIES IN 2024
- FINANCE
- GENERAL MANAGEMENT
- HUMAN RESOURCES
- INTELLIGENCE GATHERING
- TECHNOLOGY

NUMBER OF VACANCIES
100+ graduate jobs

LOCATIONS OF VACANCIES

STARTING SALARY FOR 2024
£36,733+

WORK EXPERIENCE
SUMMER INTERNSHIPS

UNIVERSITY PROMOTIONS DURING 2023-2024
Please check with your university careers service for full details of MI6's local promotions and events.

MINIMUM ENTRY REQUIREMENTS
2.2 Degree
or relevant work experience
Varies by function.
Relevant degree required for some roles.

APPLICATION DEADLINE
Varies by function

FURTHER INFORMATION
www.Top100GraduateEmployers.com
Register now for the latest news, local promotions, work experience and graduate vacancies at MI6.

JOIN THE TEAM WHO PROTECT THE UK AND HELP SHAPE WORLD EVENTS.

BECOME AN INTELLIGENCE OFFICER AT MI6.

FIND OUT MORE AT SIS.GOV.UK

SECRET INTELLIGENCE SERVICE MI6

SECRETLY, JUST LIKE YOU

EarlyCareersSky **f**   earlycareers@sky.uk ✉

@EarlyCareersSky **𝕏**   linkedin.com/company/sky **in**

@_LifeAtSky **◉**   youtube.com/workforsky **▶**

Sky is Europe's leading media and entertainment company and is proud to be part of Comcast Corporation, connecting people to the moments that matter. Across six countries, Sky connects 23 million customers to the best entertainment, sports, news, arts and their own award-winning original content.

Creating pixel perfect display and sonic boom worthy sound. Shaping the way the world experiences unmissable moments. Understanding how to make a bigger picture impact. The spark of a better idea starts at Sky, and graduates help make it all happen. A career at Sky is where better begins.

The range of early careers programmes at Sky gives new joiners the chance to own projects, to learn, grow and develop their skill set. Graduates and interns all benefit from on-the-job learning, and receive the support they need to be brilliant from day one.

Sky's range of internship programmes help build key skills and career confidence. For graduates, they offer specialist programmes across Change Delivery, Data, Software Engineering and more, where individuals learn from industry experts. Whatever their background, skills or passions, candidates can choose a career that suits them.

Sky's unique insight events give candidates a behind the scenes look into life at Sky, helping graduates make informed decisions as they take the first steps of their careers.

Sky takes pride in their approach to diversity and inclusion: they've been recognised by The Times and Stonewall for their commitment, and they've set ambitious 2025 targets to continue to improve representation across the business. They're committed to investing £30 million across markets over the next three years to invest in their inclusion strategy, and to tackle racial injustice.

GRADUATE VACANCIES IN 2024
ACCOUNTANCY
ENGINEERING
FINANCE
GENERAL MANAGEMENT
MARKETING
MEDIA
SALES
TECHNOLOGY

NUMBER OF VACANCIES
232 graduate jobs

LOCATIONS OF VACANCIES

STARTING SALARY FOR 2024
£30,000-£38,000

WORK EXPERIENCE
SUMMER INTERNSHIPS

UNIVERSITY PROMOTIONS DURING 2023-2024
ABERDEEN, BRUNEL, CITY, EDINBURGH, GLASGOW, LEEDS, SHEFFIELD, ST ANDREWS, STIRLING, STRATHCLYDE, SURREY, UNIVERSITY COLLEGE LONDON, WARWICK, YORK
Please check with your university careers service for full details of Sky's local promotions and events.

MINIMUM ENTRY REQUIREMENTS
Any degree accepted

APPLICATION DEADLINE
Varies by function

FURTHER INFORMATION
www.Top100GraduateEmployers.com
Register now for the latest news, local promotions, work experience and graduate vacancies at Sky.

Where **better** begins

We celebrate diversity. Because different people with different perspectives make Sky a better business. Our customers are incredibly diverse, so we should be too. That's why we're working hard to build an inclusive culture, where you can be yourself. Whoever you are. Wherever you're from.

Launch an exciting career with Sky, Europe's largest media company - our graduate programmes cover a wide range of exciting areas including **Business Strategy, Finance, Change Delivery, Technology, Software Engineering** and much more.

Find out all about our Early Careers opportunities at **skyearlycareers.com**

SLAUGHTER AND MAY/

slaughterandmay.com

trainee.recruit@slaughterandmay.com

@SlaughterandMayCareers

Slaughter and May is one of the most prestigious law firms in the world. The strength of their global practice is reflected both in the multi-jurisdictional nature of their work and their international client base. The firm is a trusted adviser to some of the largest global companies in the world.

There are distinct differences that set Slaughter and May apart from other global law firms. These differences are in relation to their international approach, multi-specialist training, and lack of billable targets.

Slaughter and May work with the very best law firms across the globe to support their clients, handpicked to meet the needs of each matter, to deliver integrated legal advice. Fundamental to their business model is the ability to work in partnership with other law firms – this is how they have built their successful global practice.

Slaughter and May lawyers are all trained to be multi-specialists across a broad range of legal matters. This is hard work, but their lawyers say it makes for a far more fulfilling career. It provides challenge and interest and also allows their lawyers to develop deeper relationships with clients, because they get to know their businesses better.

Their lawyers are not set billing targets. In this way, their lawyers are free to work collaboratively, sharing expertise and knowledge so that they can concentrate on what matters most – the quality of the work and client service.

Slaughter and May takes great store in drawing strength from diversity and believes that an inclusive workplace drives collaboration and enhances business performance. They are looking to employ the brightest minds regardless of what or where they studied. They offer open days, workshops, and work experience schemes to enable applicants to gain an insight into life as a commercial lawyer.

GRADUATE VACANCIES IN 2024
LAW

NUMBER OF VACANCIES
95 graduate jobs
For training contracts starting in 2026.

LOCATIONS OF VACANCIES

STARTING SALARY FOR 2024
£50,000

WORK EXPERIENCE
INSIGHT COURSES · SUMMER INTERNSHIPS

UNIVERSITY PROMOTIONS DURING 2023-2024
Please check with your university careers service for full details of Slaughter and May's local promotions and events.

MINIMUM ENTRY REQUIREMENTS
2.1 Degree

APPLICATION DEADLINE
Please see website for full details.

FURTHER INFORMATION
www.Top100GraduateEmployers.com
Register now for the latest news, local promotions, work experience and graduate vacancies at Slaughter and May.

SLAUGHTER AND MAY/

A WORLD OF DIFFERENCE

Laws, international markets, global institutions… all changing every day. So how do we, as an international law firm, create the agility of mind that enables us to guide some of the world's most influential organisations into the future?

By allowing bright people the freedom to grow. By training lawyers in a way that develops a closer understanding of clients through working on a wider range of transactions. By fostering an ethos of knowledge sharing, support and mutual development by promoting from within and leaving the clocks outside when it comes to billing. To learn more about how our key differences not only make a world of difference to our clients, but also to our lawyers and their careers, visit

slaughterandmay.com/careers

SLAUGHTER AND MAY/

95
Training Contracts

Lawyers from
65+
universities

300+
workshops
and schemes

TeachFirst recruitment@teachfirst.org.uk
@TeachFirst linkedin.com/company/teach-first
@TeachFirstUK youtube.com/TeachFirstYT

Right now, there are children in this country who won't get the education they deserve. It's not okay and it's not fair. Since 2003, Teach First have been improving the life chances for children living in disadvantaged communities by training brilliant teachers to work in the schools that need them the most.

Graduates have many career options ahead of them, but few are more meaningful than teaching. For 20 years, Teach First has been fighting to give every child the chance to fulfill their potential. It begins with getting great teachers into the schools that need them the most.

Teach First's Training Programme is the largest teacher training and leadership programme in the UK. It offers graduates a salary while they train and opens the door to a world of career possibilities. Over two years, they'll qualify as teachers, gain a fully-funded qualification, receive professional coaching worth over £10k and develop an array of transferable leadership skills.

From their first day in the classroom, trainees make an instant impact on the lives of young people, in a role where no two days are the same. With support from Teach First, trainees are seven times more likely to progress into leadership roles early in their careers. And the charity has an influential network of 15,000+ teachers and leaders as well as links to a range of organisations, many of which offer trainees extra opportunities to hone their leadership skills through coaching and summer projects.

The challenge is real, but so is the chance to create lasting change. This is the most important generation of teachers and leaders, joining Teach First to fight for a fairer future.

Visit the Teach First website to find out more and apply now. It's never too soon to start changing the future.

GRADUATE VACANCIES IN 2024
TEACHING

NUMBER OF VACANCIES
1,750 graduate jobs

LOCATIONS OF VACANCIES

STARTING SALARY FOR 2024
£Competitive

WORK EXPERIENCE
INSIGHT
COURSES

**UNIVERSITY PROMOTIONS
DURING 2023-2024**
ABERDEEN, ABERYSTWYTH, ASTON, BANGOR, BATH, BELFAST, BIRMINGHAM, BRADFORD, BRISTOL, CAMBRIDGE, CARDIFF, CITY, DURHAM, EDINBURGH, ESSEX, EXETER, GLASGOW, HERIOT-WATT, HULL, IMPERIAL COLLEGE LONDON, KEELE, KING'S COLLEGE LONDON, KENT, LANCASTER, LEEDS, LEICESTER, LIVERPOOL, LONDON SCHOOL OF ECONOMICS, LOUGHBOROUGH, MANCHESTER, NEWCASTLE, NORTHUMBRIA, NOTTINGHAM, NOTTINGHAM TRENT, OXFORD, OXFORD BROOKES, PLYMOUTH, QUEEN MARY LONDON, READING, ROYAL HOLLOWAY, SCHOOL OF AFRICAN STUDIES, SHEFFIELD, SOUTHAMPTON, ST ANDREWS, SURREY, SUSSEX, SWANSEA, UEA, UNIVERSITY COLLEGE LONDON, WARWICK, YORK

MINIMUM ENTRY REQUIREMENTS
2.1 Degree
However, all applications are assessed on a case-by-case basis.

APPLICATION DEADLINE
Year-round recruitment

FURTHER INFORMATION
www.Top100GraduateEmployers.com
Register now for the latest news, local promotions, work experience and graduate vacancies at Teach First.

Unlocked

Unlocked Graduates is a unique two-year Leadership Development Programme that puts brilliant graduates at the heart of prison reform. This award-winning programme recruits outstanding graduates and career changers to become exceptional leaders.

Nearly half of all adult prisoners reoffend within one year of leaving prison, creating more victims, untold damage, and a cost of over £18 billion. The problems facing prisons are some of the most complex in society. That is the challenge at the heart of the Unlocked Graduates two-year Leadership Development Programme. Unlocked looks for ambitious graduates who are passionate about shaping the system for the better, as well as gaining a fully funded Master's degree, a highly competitive salary, specialised mentoring and work placement opportunities with key employers. Combining academic study with real-world experience, Unlocked provides the platform to trial and assess solutions within prisons. And, in their second year, graduates get to write and present a policy paper to the Government.

Many graduates choose to stay within the justice system after they finish the programme or go on to make a difference in a variety of prestigious careers, but no matter where their career takes them, Unlocked continues to support this growing network of change-makers. With alumni attending international conferences in Lisbon and Madrid, sharing best practice with prisons in the US and Norway and winning awards such as the Prime Minister's award.

This is a chance to join the graduate Leadership Development Programme that saw participants launch award-winning innovation acceleration projects and make real changes to prisoners lives through phenomenal rehabilitative work. This is two years to become a leader. One opportunity to change society.

GRADUATE VACANCIES IN 2024
PRISON OFFICER

NUMBER OF VACANCIES
143 graduate jobs

LOCATIONS OF VACANCIES

STARTING SALARY FOR 2024
£28,000-£34,000

UNIVERSITY PROMOTIONS DURING 2023-2024
ASTON, BATH, BIRMINGHAM, BRISTOL, CAMBRIDGE, DURHAM, EDINBURGH, EXETER, KING'S COLLEGE LONDON, KENT, LEEDS, LEICESTER, LONDON SCHOOL OF ECONOMICS, LOUGHBOROUGH, MANCHESTER, NOTTINGHAM, OXFORD, SHEFFIELD, SOUTHAMPTON, UNIVERSITY COLLEGE LONDON, WARWICK, YORK
Please check with your university careers service for full details of Unlocked's local promotions and events.

MINIMUM ENTRY REQUIREMENTS
2.1 Degree

APPLICATION DEADLINE
January 2024
Early application is advised.

FURTHER INFORMATION
www.Top100GraduateEmployers.com
Register now for the latest news, local promotions, work experience and graduate vacancies at Unlocked.

"It's a fantastic opportunity to develop as a person, as a professional and as a leader.

With Unlocked Graduates, I was put in positions very early on where I had to organise a team. I learned to lead the people I was looking after in that environment and learned so many skills in working with different personalities as well as managing expectations and challenges. Following my two years on the Unlocked programme, I now work as a Senior Policy Advisor for the Civil Service.

Unlocked

unlockedgrads.org.uk

 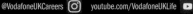

Vodafone connects people, businesses, and their devices to help everyone benefit from digital innovation. From sending the first ever text message and making the first 5G call, to covering 99% of the population with their 4G network, they have a proven track record as a pioneer of inclusive and sustainable digital societies.

The business' purpose is to connect for a better future by using technology to improve lives. They believe in the power of connectivity for their 18 million customers in the UK, and their 300 million customers in 17 countries worldwide.

Vodafone are passionate about creating a better future, with the belief that when working together, humanity and technology can find answers and break new ground to achieve great feats. Most recently this has seen them power IoT that connects over 160 million devices and platforms, powering 100% of the grid electricity they use in the UK from certified renewable sources and partnering with organisations to close the digital divide in the UK and give vulnerable people access to mobile and broadband.

At Vodafone, graduates are inspired to experiment, develop new skills, and make mistakes…after all, it's the fastest way to learn. Vodafone's Discover Graduate programme enables talented young minds to gain hands-on experience, technical skills, personal and professional growth; and the opportunity to learn from industry experts in an environment which is diverse, inclusive, and nurturing. Graduates can gain experience in tech, finance, strategy, marketing, commercial, and HR.

Vodafone welcomes innovators, collaborators and those who are open-minded and aren't afraid to push boundaries. Start a career with Vodafone and make a positive impact. More information about Vodafone is available at their graduate website.

GRADUATE VACANCIES IN 2024

FINANCE
GENERAL MANAGEMENT
HUMAN RESOURCES
MARKETING
SALES
TECHNOLOGY

NUMBER OF VACANCIES
100+ graduate jobs

LOCATIONS OF VACANCIES

STARTING SALARY FOR 2024
£32,000-£35,000
Plus an annual bonus.

UNIVERSITY PROMOTIONS DURING 2023-2024
BIRMINGHAM, BRUNEL, IMPERIAL COLLEGE LONDON, KING'S COLLEGE LONDON, LEICESTER, MANCHESTER, NOTTINGHAM, QUEEN MARY LONDON, READING, SURREY, UNIVERSITY COLLEGE LONDON, WARWICK
Please check with your university careers service for full details of Vodafone's local promotions and events.

MINIMUM ENTRY REQUIREMENTS
2.2 Degree

APPLICATION DEADLINE
Varies by function

FURTHER INFORMATION
www.Top100GraduateEmployers.com
Register now for the latest news, local promotions, work experience and graduate vacancies at Vodafone.

Can your ideas go from virtual to viral?

Discover our graduate careers

Make an impact that matters

Join us and you'll have the chance to explore all the exciting possibilities a Vodafone career can offer. And while you're doing that, your contribution will make a real difference too.

careers.vodafone.co.uk/graduate-programme

Together we can

WHITE & CASE

GRADUATE VACANCIES IN 2024
LAW

NUMBER OF VACANCIES
50 graduate jobs
For training contracts starting in 2026.

LOCATIONS OF VACANCIES

STARTING SALARY FOR 2024
£52,000

WORK EXPERIENCE
INSIGHT COURSES | DEGREE PLACEMENTS | SUMMER INTERNSHIPS

UNIVERSITY PROMOTIONS DURING 2023-2024
Please check with your university careers service for full details of White & Case's local promotions and events.

MINIMUM ENTRY REQUIREMENTS
2.1 Degree

APPLICATION DEADLINE
Please see website for full details.

FURTHER INFORMATION
www.Top100GraduateEmployers.com
Register now for the latest news, local promotions, work experience and graduate vacancies at White & Case.

White & Case is a global law firm of more than 2,500 lawyers worldwide. They've built an unrivalled network of 45 offices in 31 countries. That investment is the foundation for their client work in over 200 countries today. Many White & Case clients are multinational organisations with complex needs that require the involvement of multiple offices.

White & Case trainees will work on fast-paced, cutting-edge cross-border projects from the outset of their career. White & Case is looking to recruit ambitious trainees who have a desire to gain hands-on practical experience from day one and a willingness to take charge of their own career. They value globally minded citizens of the world who are eager to work across borders and cultures, and who are intrigued by solving problems within multiple legal systems.

The training contract consists of four six-month seats, one of which is guaranteed to be spent in one of their overseas offices.

They offer vacation scheme placements over the winter, spring, and summer, open days, and two-day insight schemes. These provide a great way to experience first-hand what life is like as a White & Case trainee as well as gain useful insight into the firm and the training they offer.

The firm's virtual learning programme offers the opportunity to gain first-hand insight into life as a White & Case trainee and experience the realities of cross-border law. There is no cost to access the platform, it is self-paced to fit around users' schedules, and no application form or legal knowledge is required. Students will gain insight into the fast-paced, cutting-edge projects their lawyers and trainees work on, and gain valuable skills by undertaking true-to-life legal tasks. Participation in the learning platform will be recognised on their application forms.

Together we make a mark

Graduate careers in law

As a trainee in our London office, you will have the opportunity to work on challenging cross-border client matters providing you with international experience and exposure from day one. Join us and make your mark.

whitecasetrainee.com

1	**75**	**£52k**
of the only law firms to offer a guaranteed overseas seat	vacation scheme places per year in London	year-one starting salary

45	**50**	**£140k**
offices across 31 countries	trainees recruited per year in London	salary on qualification

WHITE & CASE

Useful Information

EMPLOYER	GRADUATE RECRUITMENT WEBSITE	EMPLOYER	GRADUATE RECRUITMENT WEBSITE
AECOM	aecom.com/uk-ireland-graduate-careers	IBM	ibm.biz/graduate
AIRBUS	airbus.com/careers	J.P. MORGAN	jpmorgan.com/careers
ALDI	aldirecruitment.co.uk	KPMG	kpmgcareers.co.uk/graduate
AMAZON	amazon.jobs/student-programs	KUBRICK	kubrickgroup.com/uk
AON	aon.com/careers/early-careers/uk	L'ORÉAL	careers.loreal.com
ARCADIS	careers.arcadis.com/locations/uk/ey	LATHAM & WATKINS	lwcareers.com/london-graduate-opportunities
ASTRAZENECA	careers.astrazeneca.com/early-talent	LIDL	lidlgraduatecareers.co.uk
BAE SYSTEMS	baesystems.com/graduates	LINKLATERS	careers.linklaters.com
BANK OF AMERICA	campus.bankofamerica.com	LLOYDS BANKING GROUP	lloydsbankinggrouptalent.com
BARCLAYS	search.jobs.barclays	MARS	careers.mars.com/uk/en/students-graduates
BBC	careers.bbc.co.uk	MAZARS	jobs.mazars.co.uk/jobs/early-careers
BCG	careers.bcg.com	MI5 - THE SECURITY SERVICE	mi5.gov.uk/careers
BDO	careers.bdo.co.uk	MICROSOFT	careers.microsoft.com/students
BLACKROCK	careers.blackrock.com/early-careers	MORGAN STANLEY	morganstanley.com/campus
BLOOMBERG	bloomberg.com/company/what-we-do	MOTT MACDONALD	mottmac.com/careers
BRITISH AIRWAYS	careers.ba.com/graduates	NATWEST GROUP	jobs.natwestgroup.com
BT GROUP	jobs.bt.com/content/students-and-graduates/	NEWTON	workatnewton.com
CAPGEMINI	capgemini.com/gb-en/careers/career-paths	NGDP	local.gov.uk/ngdp
CHANNEL 4	careers.channel4.com/4skills	NHS	graduates.nhs.uk
CITI	oncampus.citi.com	P&G	pgcareers.com/location-uk-and-ireland
CIVIL SERVICE FAST STREAM	faststream.gov.uk	PENGUIN	penguinrandomhousecareers.co.uk
CLYDE & CO	clydecoearlycareers.com	PFIZER	pfizer.co.uk/careers
CMS	cmsearlytalent.com	POLICE NOW	policenow.org.uk
DELOITTE	deloitte.co.uk/careers	PWC	pwc.co.uk/careers
DEUTSCHE BANK	careers.db.com/students-graduates	ROLLS-ROYCE	careers.rolls-royce.com
DLA PIPER	earlycareers.dlapiper.com	ROYAL NAVY	royalnavy.mod.uk/careers
DYSON	careers.dyson.com/early-careers	SANTANDER	santander.com/en/careers/uk-careers
ENTERPRISE	careers.enterprise.co.uk	SAVILLS	savills.co.uk/apply/current-graduate-vacancies.aspx
EY	ey.com/uk/students	SECRET INTELLIGENCE SERVICE (MI6)	sis.gov.uk/explore-careers.html
FRESHFIELDS	freshfields.com/ukgraduates	SKY	careers.sky.com/earlycareers
FRONTLINE	thefrontline.org.uk/frontline-programme	SLAUGHTER AND MAY	slaughterandmay.com
GOOGLE	google.com/students	TEACH FIRST	teachfirst.org.uk/training-programme
GRANT THORNTON	trainees.grantthornton.co.uk	UNLOCKED	unlockedgrads.org.uk
GSK	gsk.com/en-gb/careers	VODAFONE	careers.vodafone.com/uk/graduate-opportunities
HOGAN LOVELLS	graduates.hoganlovells.com	WHITE & CASE	whitecasetrainee.com
HSBC	hsbc.com/earlycareers		